Framework
SCIENCE

Sarah Jagger

Foundations

OXFORD
UNIVERSITY PRESS

Great Clarendon Street, Oxford OX2 6DP

Oxford University Press is a department of the University of Oxford.
It furthers the University's objective of excellence in research, scholarship,
and education by publishing worldwide in

Oxford New York

Auckland Cape Town Dar es Salaam Hong Kong Karachi
Kuala Lumpur Madrid Melbourne Mexico City Nairobi
New Delhi Shanghai Taipei Toronto

With offices in

Argentina Austria Brazil Chile Czech Republic France Greece
Guatemala Hungary Italy Japan South Korea Poland Portugal
Singapore Switzerland Thailand Turkey Ukraine Vietnam

Oxford is a registered trade mark of Oxford University Press
in the UK and in certain other countries

British Library Cataloguing in Publication Data

Data available

ISBN 0 19 915007 9

ISBN 978 019 915007 6

1 3 5 7 9 10 8 6 4 2

Printed in Italy by Rotolito Lombarda

Acknowledgements

The Publisher would like to thank the following for permission to
reproduce photographs:

P22 Custom Medical Stock Photo/Corbis UK Ltd; **p25** Digital Stock/Corbis
UK Ltd/OUP; **p29** Sami Sarkis/Alamy; **p30l** Photodisc/OUP; **p30cl** Simon
Fraser/Science Photo Library; **p30cr** Digital Stock/Corbis UK Ltd/OUP; **p30r**
Erik Crichton/Corbis UK Ltd; **p31** Graham Burns/Photofusion Picture
Library/Alamy; **p38** Pictor International/ImageState/Alamy; **p40** Photodisc/
OUP; **p44t&b** Martyn F Chillmaid; **p45t** Martyn F Chillmaid; **p45b** Andrew
Lambert Photography/Science Photo Library; **p50l&r** Geoscience Features
Picture Library; **p51** Geophotos; **p54** Kevin Schafer/Corbis UK Ltd; **p57l &r**
Geoscience Features Picture Library; **p58t** Geophotos; **p58b** George H H
Huey/Corbis UK Ltd; **p59t** Geoscience Features Picture Library; **p59b** Ric
Ergenbright/corbis UK Ltd; **p60t** Geoscience Features Pocture Library; **p60b**
H D Thoreau/Corbis UK Ltd; **p65** Photodisc/OUP; **p73** Cordelia Molloy/
Science Photo Library; **p80** Corel/OUP; **p89** Dan Sinclair/Zooid Pictures

Technical illustrations are by Oxford Designers and Illustrators

Cartoons are by John Hallet

Front cover photos: Corbis UK Ltd and Pictor

Contents

Introduction

Everyone in school does science because it helps us make decisions about our everyday lives. For example: Which foods should we eat if we want to be healthy? Is it safe to use a mobile phone? Science is also fun, and by studying science we get to find out how things work. This book is designed to help you learn about the key ideas in science that are taught in Year 8. We hope that you enjoy it.

How to use this book

This book is divided into 12 topics:

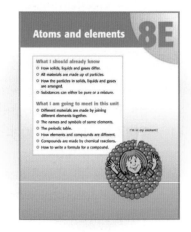

○ At the start of each topic you will find an **opener page**. This page will remind you of what you already know about a topic, and will introduce the key ideas that you are about to meet.

○ At the bottom of each main page there are some **questions** for you to test your understanding. Most of them can be answered using the information on the page, but some will require you to use your thinking skills and apply what you have just learnt. These questions are indicated by a thought bubble like this one:

○ At the end of each topic there is a '**What have I learnt?**' page, with questions for you to test yourself.

○ If you want to find out about something in particular use the **Contents** or the **Index**.

○ The **Glossary** explains what certain words mean.

Food and digestion

What I should already know

- Sailors used to get scurvy because they had poor diets.
- A healthy diet doesn't contain too much fat or sugar.
- The names of some organs, and what they do.
- Everything around us is made up of particles.

What I am going to meet in this unit

- Why we need nutrients from food.
- We need a balanced diet to be healthy.
- Carbohydrates, fats and proteins.
- Food is broken down by the digestive system.
- Nutrients from food are transported around the body by the blood.
- Enzymes break nutrients up into small pieces.

You are what you eat ...

Marvo
The Amazing
Sword Swallower

Without food our bodies don't work properly. We need to eat food so that our bodies can **grow**, **repair** damaged cells and **move**. Different foods contain different nutrients. There are seven different nutrients. We need to eat all of them to stay healthy:

- Protein
- Fat
- Minerals
- Water
- Carbohydrates
- Vitamins
- Fibre

Vegetables and bread contain **fibre**.

Drinks and most foods contain **water**.

Bread, pasta and rice are rich in **carbohydrates**.

Fruit, juices and vegetables contain **vitamins**.

Salt and cheese contain **minerals**.

Fish, eggs, meat and cheese provide **protein**.

Ice cream, sweets, cheese and oil contain **fats**.

All of the seven nutrients are found in this meal.

1 What three things do our bodies need food for?

2 Unscramble these words:

taf   tenipor   ribef   ratew

3 Describe what you ate for dinner yesterday. Which nutrients did you get from your meal. Which nutrients were missing from your meal? Did you drink any water?

Copy and complete using these words:

protein   cells   nutrients

water   grow   fat

Our bodies need _____ from food to be able to _____, repair damaged _____ and move. The seven nutrients are _____, carbohydrates, _____, fibre, vitamins, minerals and _____. We need all of them to stay healthy.

To be **healthy** we need to eat a **balanced diet**. This means that we need to eat enough of each of the seven **nutrients**, but we should also be careful not to eat too much of them. Different people need different amounts of each nutrient depending on what they do.

These people need different diets to stay healthy.

This food guide pyramid shows us which foods should make up most of our diet. It also shows us which foods we should only eat a little of. Foods that are rich in carbohydrates should make up the biggest part of our diet. Foods that are rich in fats and sugar should make up the smallest part of our diet.

foods rich in fat and sugar

foods rich in protein

foods rich in vitamins and minerals

foods rich in carbohydrates

1 What do we mean when we say that we need to eat a balanced diet?

2 Which type of foods should make up the biggest part of our diet?

3 Draw your own food guide pyramid. Write examples of foods that contain the relevant nutrients in each section. Use the picture of the food guide pyramid above to help you. Try to think of some new examples.

Copy and complete using these words:

nutrient   balanced   fats   seven carbohydrates   biggest

To have a _____ diet we need to eat enough of each of the _____ nutrients. Different people need different amounts of each _____ in their diet. Foods that are rich in _____ should make up the _____ part of our diet. Foods that are rich in _____ should make up the smallest part.

Our bodies have to break down the food that we eat so that we can use the nutrients in it. This process is called **digestion**. Digestion happens in the **digestive system**.

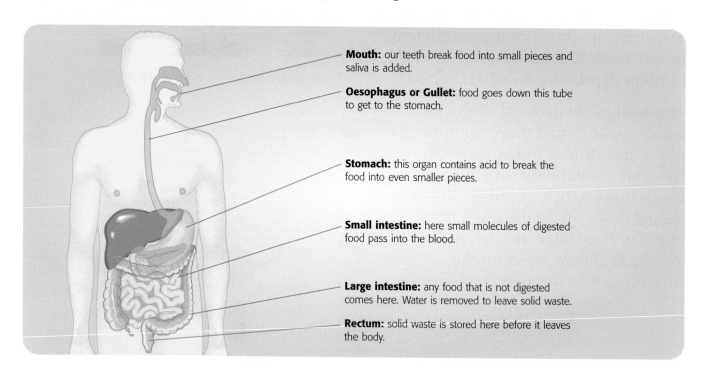

Mouth: our teeth break food into small pieces and saliva is added.

Oesophagus or Gullet: food goes down this tube to get to the stomach.

Stomach: this organ contains acid to break the food into even smaller pieces.

Small intestine: here small molecules of digested food pass into the blood.

Large intestine: any food that is not digested comes here. Water is removed to leave solid waste.

Rectum: solid waste is stored here before it leaves the body.

1 What do we call the process by which our food is broken down?

2 These words have had their vowels removed. What should they say?

stmch   mth   smll ntstn   gllt

3 Which part of the digestive system does digested food pass through to get into the blood? What happens to food that is not digested?

Copy and complete using these words:

**blood   large   digestive   waste
digestion   small**

Food is broken down by _____. This happens in the _____ system. During digestion, nutrients are absorbed into the _____ through the wall of the _____ intestine. Anything that can't be digested passes through the _____ intestine to the rectum, and leaves the body as _____.

How is food broken down?

During digestion, **large insoluble** molecules are broken down into molecules that are **small** and **soluble** (dissolve in water). Most vitamins and minerals are small molecules, but carbohydrates, proteins and fats are very large. They must be broken down into smaller molecules before they can pass into the blood and be used by the body.

Our bodies make special molecules called **enzymes** to cut large, insoluble molecules into small pieces. Each enzyme cuts up a different type of food molecule.

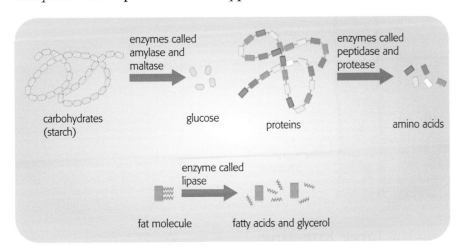

1 Name a nutrient that is small and doesn't need to be broken down during digestion.

2 Unscramble these words:

   carsth   tfa   zenmey   tripeno

3 Think about what an enzyme does. Try to explain how an enzyme is like a pair of scissors. You may find it helpful to draw a picture to go with your answer.

Copy and complete using these words:

**enzymes   insoluble   carbohydrates
blood   soluble   fats**

During digestion, large _____ molecules are broken down into small _____ molecules. _____, proteins and _____ are very large. Our bodies make special molecules called _____ to cut them up into small pieces. They can then pass into the _____ and be used by the body.

Trillions of chemical reactions happen in the cells of your body every second. All of these chemical reactions use digested food molecules.

The walls of the **small intestine** are very thin. Small soluble molecules of digested food are **absorbed** (taken in) by them and pass into the **blood**. The blood then takes these molecules to all of the **cells** in the body, where they are used in chemical reactions like respiration or reactions that help us grow.

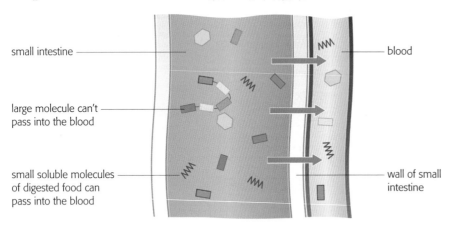

small intestine

large molecule can't pass into the blood

small soluble molecules of digested food can pass into the blood

blood

wall of small intestine

Fibre and waste products pass into the **large intestine** before leaving the body. Although we can't digest fibre, we need to eat it to keep our intestines healthy.

1 Which of the seven nutrients can't be digested?

2 What do we mean when we say that something is absorbed?

3 Make a list of foods that are rich in fibre. What happens to fibre during digestion? Why do we need to eat fibre-rich foods?

Copy and complete using these words:

blood   small   absorbed   waste

Small molecules of digested food are _____ through the wall of the _____ intestine. They pass into the _____. They can then be use in chemical reactions. Food that is not digested leaves the body as _____.

What have I learnt?

1 Imagine that you ate nothing but chips for a month. Why wouldn't this be good for you? Which nutrients would be missing from your diet?

2 Match up the beginnings and endings below to make complete sentences.

Beginnings

Healthy eating means

Foods rich in carbohydrate

Foods rich in fats and sugar

Different people need

Endings

should make up the biggest part of your diet.

different diets to stay healthy.

should make up the smallest part of your diet.

eating the right amounts of each of the seven nutrients.

3 Write the sentences below in the correct order to describe what happens during digestion:

o Water is removed from undigested food.

o Acid is added in the stomach.

o Solid waste is stored before it leaves the body.

o Food is broken down by the teeth and saliva.

o Small molecules of digested food pass into the blood.

4 Why must proteins be broken down before they can be used by cells in the body?

5 Match each organ of the digestive system with the correct description of what happens there during digestion:

Organs

Small intestine

Stomach

Large intestine

Mouth

What happens there

Acid is added to break down food.

Water is removed from undigested food to form solid waste.

Food is chewed and saliva is added.

Small molecules of digested food pass into the blood.

6 Pasta is rich in carbohydrates and also contains fibre. Write a story to describe what happens to pasta as it passes through your digestive system. Use these questions to help you:

o Which parts of the digestive system does the pasta pass through?

o What happens to the pasta in each part of the digestive system?

o Will some of the pasta molecules be cut up by an enzyme?

o Will all of the pasta be digested?

Respiration

What I should already know

- Digested food is transported around the body by the blood.
- Living organisms need energy.
- A food label shows how much energy is in a food.
- Carbon dioxide is produced when a fuel burns.

What I am going to meet in this unit

- All living things respire.
- Plants and animals need oxygen to produce energy by aerobic respiration.
- Oxygen and glucose are transported around the body by the blood.
- The circulatory and respiratory systems.
- How inhaled air and exhaled air differ.
- What happens if too little oxygen reaches our tissues.

All of the cells in our body need **nutrients** from our **food**. **Digested** food is used for **growth**, **repairing** old or damaged cells and **energy**.

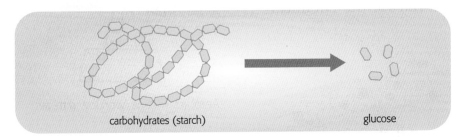

carbohydrates (starch)   glucose

Starch (a carbohydrate) is a large insoluble molecule that is broken down into glucose molecules during digestion. The small soluble glucose molecules can then pass into the blood and travel to all of the cells in our bodies.

Our cells use glucose in a chemical reaction called **aerobic respiration**. **Oxygen** is needed for this reaction and **energy** is released. We need this energy so that we can move and make heat to keep our bodies warm. All living things respire.

glucose + oxygen → carbon dioxide + water This releases energy.

---

1 What are the nutrients from our food used for?

2 Unscramble these words:

partinoseri   goescul   greeny

3 Write a word equation for the aerobic respiration reaction. Energy is produced by this reaction. What do we need this energy for?

Copy and complete using these words:

energy   starch   carbon dioxide
glucose   respiration   oxygen

_____ is broken down into _____ molecules during digestion. Our cells use glucose and _____ in a chemical reaction called aerobic _____. The products of respiration are _____ _____ and water. _____ is released.

Cells need both oxygen and glucose to make energy by **respiration**. Glucose is a store of **chemical energy**. The reaction is called **aerobic** (with air) respiration because oxygen from the air is needed to release the chemical energy from glucose.

Aerobics means 'working with air'.

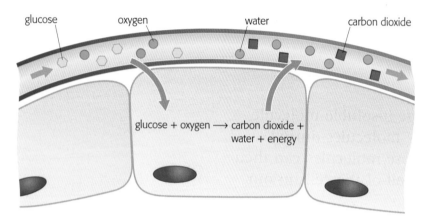

glucose + oxygen ⟶ carbon dioxide + water + energy

The cells in your body use glucose and oxygen to make energy by aerobic respiration. Carbon dioxide and water are also produced. They are carried away from the cells by the blood.

When we exercise, the cells in our muscles respire faster. They need more oxygen so your heart pumps faster. You breathe faster too. If you exercise very hard for a long time your muscle cells can't get enough oxygen to respire. You get **muscle fatigue** (very tired muscles) and may also get **cramp**. If you exercise gently you can keep going for a long time because your muscle cells can easily get all the oxygen that they need.

1 What does 'aerobic' mean?

2 What are the products of aerobic respiration?

3 Imagine that you tried to sprint for an hour. How long would you be able to keep going without getting muscle fatigue? What would happen to your muscle cells? Explain why this would happen.

Copy and complete using these words:

cramp **oxygen** **fatigue**
glucose **aerobic**

Both _____ and oxygen are needed for _____ respiration. When we exercise our muscle cells need more _____. Our heart pumps faster and we breathe faster. If our muscle cells can't get enough oxygen we get muscle _____ and may get _____.

How oxygen reaches cells

Oxygen and nutrients like glucose are carried around our bodies by our blood. Blood is part of the **circulatory system**, the organ system that transports things around our bodies.

1 The **heart** pumps blood to the **lungs**, where it picks up oxygen and gets rid of carbon dioxide. The blood is now **oxygenated** (has lots of oxygen in it).

2 The oxygenated blood goes back to the heart.

3 The heart pumps oxygenated blood all around the body to other **organs**.

4 In the tissues, oxygen and glucose go into the **cells** for respiration. The blood is now **deoxygenated** (has less oxygen in it). Carbon dioxide and other wastes go into the blood to be taken away.

5 The deoxygenated blood is pumped back to the heart and the cycle starts again.

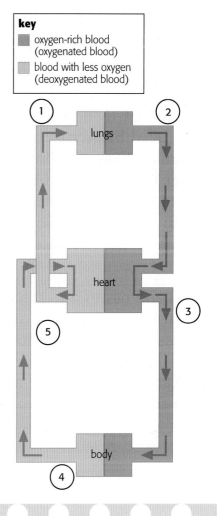

key
oxygen-rich blood (oxygenated blood)
blood with less oxygen (deoxygenated blood)

1 What do we call the organ system that transports things around our bodies?

2 These words have had their vowels removed. What should they say?
hrt   lngs   dxygntd   clls

3 What is the difference between oxygenated and deoxygenated blood? Draw a picture to show how oxygenated and deoxygenated blood travel around the body. Remember to label the parts of the body that are involved.

Copy and complete using these words:

**respiration   heart   deoxygenated
wastes   oxygenated   circulatory**

Blood is part of the _____ system. The heart pumps blood to the lungs where it becomes _____. It then goes back to the _____ and is pumped all around the body. Oxygen and glucose go into cells for _____. The blood is now _____. Carbon dioxide and other _____ go into the blood to be taken away.

What do the lungs do?

The **lungs** are part of the **respiratory** (breathing) **system**. They are specialised to exchange gases like oxygen and carbon dioxide.

The **trachea** (windpipe) splits into two tubes called **bronchi**. Each of these tubes goes into a lung. The bronchi divide into smaller branches called **bronchioles**. At the end of the bronchioles are the **alveoli** (air sacs). These have very thin walls and a large surface area.

As we breathe in, oxygen goes into the alveoli and passes into the blood. The oxygen is exchanged for carbon dioxide that has been produced during respiration. Carbon dioxide leaves the blood and passes into the alveoli. It leaves the body as we breathe out.

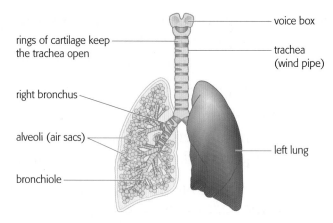

The structure of the lungs.

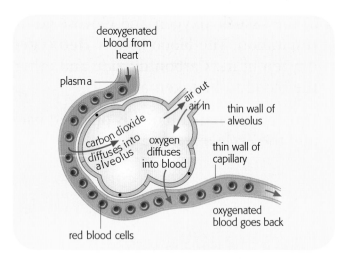

Gas exchange happens in the alveoli.

1 What is the correct name for the breathing system?

2 Unscramble these words:

heartac   chinrob   valleoi

3 Draw and label a diagram to explain how oxygen and carbon dioxide are exchanged in the alveoli. Use the diagram above to help you.

Copy and complete using these words:

**respiratory   breathe   exchange
alveoli   blood**

The lungs are part of the _____ system. They are specialised to _____ gases. In the _____, oxygen passes into the blood. Carbon dioxide passes out of the _____, and leaves the body as we _____ out.

We must be careful not to confuse breathing and respiration. Respiration is a chemical reaction that releases energy. Breathing (**ventilation**) happens when our lungs expand and contract to **inhale** (breathe in) and **exhale** (breathe out) air.

Inhaled and exhaled air are different. When we inhale, we take in **oxygen** to be used by cells for respiration. When we exhale, we get rid of poisonous **carbon dioxide** that has been produced during respiration. There is more oxygen in the air that we inhale than the air that we exhale. There is more carbon dioxide in the air that we exhale.

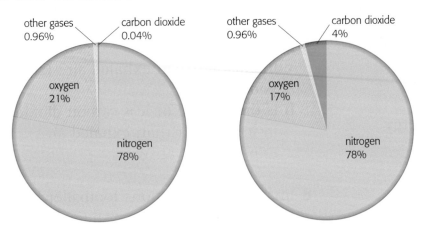

1 Is there more oxygen in inhaled air or exhaled air?

2 These words have had their vowels removed. What should they say?

brthng   rsprtn   vntltn

(3) How could you show that there is carbon dioxide in exhaled air? Think back to the work that you did in Year 7 and design a simple experiment.

Copy and complete using these words:

**respiration   exhale   ventilation
oxygen   inhale   contract**

Breathing is also known as _____. This is when our lungs expand and _____ to inhale and _____ air. There is more _____ in the air that we _____ than the air that we exhale, because oxygen is used for _____. There is more carbon dioxide in the air that we exhale.

What have I learnt?

1 Unscramble the word equation for aerobic respiration. What are the reactants for the reaction? What are the products?

energy + oxygen + carbon dioxide → glucose + water

2 Match up the beginnings and endings below to make complete sentences.

Beginnings

'Aerobic respiration' means

The reactants in aerobic respiration are

The products of aerobic respiration are

If our muscle cells can't get enough oxygen

Endings

water, carbon dioxide and energy (which is released).

we may get cramp.

respiration with air.

glucose and oxygen.

3 Write the sentences below in the correct order to describe how the circulatory system works:

o The heart pumps the oxygenated blood to cells all around the body.

o The heart pumps blood to the lungs where it becomes oxygenated.

o The deoxygenated blood returns to the heart.

o Oxygen and glucose pass into the cells, whilst carbon dioxide and water pass into the blood.

4 Copy this diagram of the lungs. Use the words below to complete the labels.

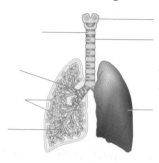

voice box   **right bronchus**
rings of cartilage   **left lung**
alveoli   **trachea**   **brochiole**

5 a Is there more or less oxygen in inhaled air than exhaled air? Explain your answer.

b Is there more or less carbon dioxide in inhaled air than exhaled air? Explain your answer.

6 Imagine that a famous footballer had cramp during a game at the weekend. You have been asked to write and article for a newspaper to explain what happened. Your article should include answers to the questions below. Try to include at least one diagram in your article, to explain what happened.

o What is aerobic respiration?

o Why do we breathe faster when we exercise?

o What happens to your muscle cells if you exercise hard for a long time?

o Why does this happen?

What I should already know

- Diseases can be passed on by very small organisms.
- The names of some illnesses, like chicken pox.
- Micro-organisms help things to decay.
- Micro-organisms are living things that grow and reproduce.
- Like us, most micro-organisms respire aerobically and produce carbon dioxide.

What I am going to meet in this unit

- Different types of micro-organism.
- Infectious diseases can be caught from other people.
- How micro-organisms get into our bodies.
- Some medicines kill micro-organisms.
- How our bodies defend us against micro-organisms that can make us ill.
- How immunisation protects us from some infectious diseases.

Over here. I've found a pathogen!

Great! I'm starving!

What are micro-organisms?

Micro-organisms (microbes) are living organisms that are too small to be seen unless you use a microscope. There are three types of micro-organism:

	Viruses	Bacteria	Fungi
What do they look like?	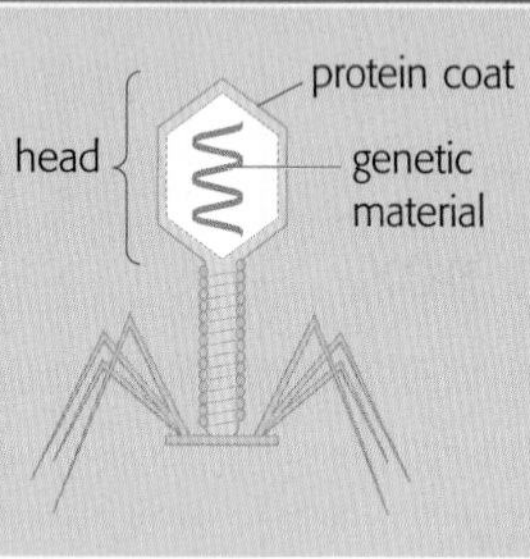 head protein coat, genetic material	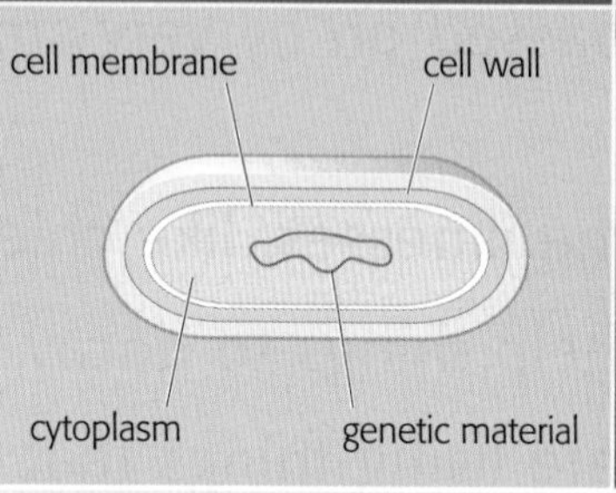 cell membrane, cell wall, cytoplasm, genetic material	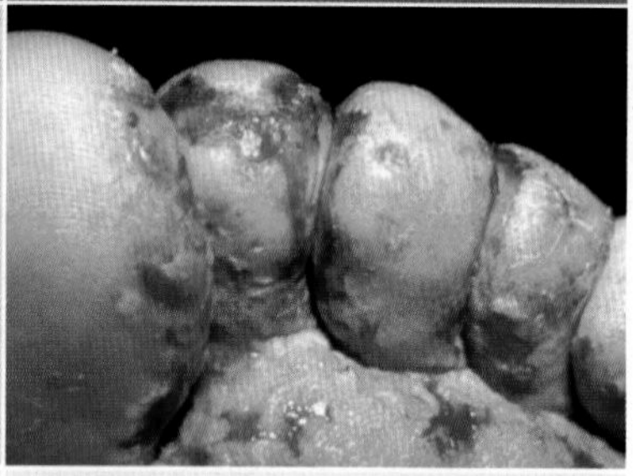
Shape	Usually regular and geometric.	Varies.	Varies.
Size	1/1000 000 mm (that's a millionth of a millimetre!).	1/1000 mm.	Varies, but most are bigger than bacteria.
Structure	Genetic material surrounded by a protein coat. Viruses are not cells.	Single-celled organisms that don't have a nucleus.	Feed off other living organisms. Some fungi send out threads.
Examples	Common cold virus, influenza (flu) virus, chickenpox virus and HIV (causes AIDS).	*Salmonella* (causes food poisoning), *Streptococcus* can cause sore throats) and *Lactobacillus* (used to make yoghurt).	Athlete's foot fungus, yeast and *Penicillium* (makes an antibiotic called penicillin).

1 Which of the three types of micro-organism is the smallest?

2 Unscramble these words:

reactabi   **gunfi**   **risesuv**

3 How do bacteria and viruses differ? Draw pictures of them as part of your answer.

Copy and complete using these words:

micro-organism   **bacteria**
microscope   **viruses**

Micro-organisms are too small to be seen unless you use a _____. The three types of _____ are viruses, _____ and fungi. _____ are the smallest and are not cells.

Diseases make people ill. Some diseases can't be passed from one person to another. Other diseases are **infectious**. You can catch them from someone else. Infectious diseases are caused when microbes (micro-organisms) get into our bodies and attack them.

How do microbes get into our bodies?

Not all microbes cause disease. Those that do are called **pathogens**. Different pathogens can be **transmitted** (passed) from person to person in different ways:

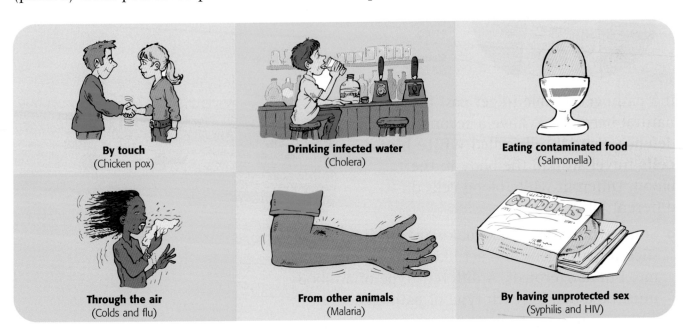

By touch
(Chicken pox)

Drinking infected water
(Cholera)

Eating contaminated food
(Salmonella)

Through the air
(Colds and flu)

From other animals
(Malaria)

By having unprotected sex
(Syphilis and HIV)

1 How is cholera transmitted?
2 These words have had their vowels removed. What should they say?
chcknpx   fl   slmnll   mlr   syphls
3 What is a pathogen? Write down six ways that pathogens can get into our bodies.

Copy and complete using these words:
microbes   infectious   pathogens

_____ diseases can be passed from one person to another. They are caused when _____ get into the body and attack it. Microbes that cause infectious diseases are called _____.

How do our bodies protect us?

Our bodies are able to protect us against pathogens most of the time. Their first lines of defence are called **natural barriers**.

Tears contain an enzyme called lysozume that kills bacteria.

Sticky **mucus** in the nose, throat and lungs traps microbes that we breathe in.

Skin stops microbes getting into our bodies. If we cut ourselves, our blood clots to seal the wound.

Stomach acid kills most of the microbes in our food.

If a pathogen is able to get past these natural barriers we have a second line of defence. Special cells called **white blood cells** travel around the body in the blood. Different white blood cells do different jobs:

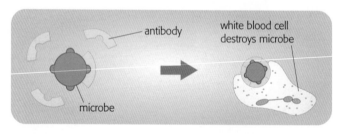

antibody

microbe

white blood cell destroys microbe

o Some white blood cells make **antibodies**. These stick to pathogens and act like signs saying 'attack me, I'm dangerous!'. A different type of antibody must be made for each type of pathogen.

o Other white blood cells **engulf** (eat) and destroy pathogens that have antibodies stuck to them.

1 Give two examples of natural barriers.

2 Unscramble these words:

togahepn   **iodniteabs**

3 Describe two ways that white blood cells protect us against pathogens. Draw a picture to show how they do this.

Copy and complete using these words:

antibodies   **engulf**   **white blood**

If a pathogen gets past natural barriers like skin we are also protected by _____ _____ cells. Some white blood cells produce _____. Others _____ and destroy pathogens.

There are things that we can do to stop the spread of **infectious diseases**. They work by stopping microbes growing, or by killing them.

Sterilisation

Microbes are killed at high temperatures. We can sterilise things by heating them to around 120 °C. When milk is **pasteurised** it is heated to a high temperature to kill any microbes that are in it. This makes it safe for us to drink.

Disinfectants

These are chemicals that kill microbes. We use them outside the body.

Chlorine is a disinfectant. It is added to cleaning products, and water in swimming pools.

Antibiotics

These are drugs that kill microbes in your body, or stop them growing. The first antibiotic, penicillin, was discovered in 1928. Antibiotics do not work on viruses.

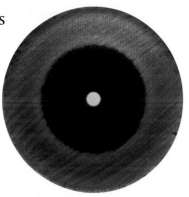

The white disc contains penicillin. The black area shows where it has killed bacteria that were growing on the plate.

1 How does sterilisation work?

2 These words have had their vowels removed. What should they say?

ntbtcs   **dsnfctnt**   **pstrsd**

3 Flu is caused by the influenza virus. Should you ask your doctor for antibiotics if you get flu? Explain your answer.

Copy and complete using these words:

antibiotics   **sterilisation**
pasteurisation   **disinfectants**

_____ kills microbes when things are heated to high temperatures. _____ is an example of this. _____ are chemicals that kill microbes. _____ are drugs that kill microbes other than viruses.

When a pathogen gets into your body, your white blood cells make antibodies so that it gets destroyed. Once antibodies have been made against the pathogen, your white blood cells 'remember' how to make them. If that type of pathogen gets into your body again your body is ready to fight it. You are **immune** to the disease.

Natural immunity

You can be naturally immune to a disease if your body has made antibodies to protect you from it before. Babies can also get some antibodies from their mothers through the placenta, and in breast milk.

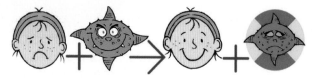

Artificial Immunity

A **vaccine** is an injection of weak or dead microbes, or bits of microbes. They don't make you ill, but your body makes **antibodies** against them. If you are infected with the disease-causing version of the microbe, you don't get ill because your white blood cells remember how to fight it.

1 What do we mean when we say that someone is immune to a disease?

2 These words have had their vowels removed. What should they say?

   mmn   **njctn**   **vccn**

3 What is a vaccine? How does a vaccine make you artificially immune to an infectious disease?

Copy and complete using these words:

vaccine   **naturally**   **artificially**
antibodies   **immune**

If you are _____ to a disease, your white blood cells remember how to make _____ against the microbe that causes it. You can be _____ immune to a disease if you have had it before. A _____ can give you _____ immunity.

What have I learnt?

1 Match the infectious diseases below to the types of microbe that cause them:

Infectious disease
Athlete's foot
Salmonella
HIV

Type of microbe
Virus
Fungi
Bacteria

2 List six ways that infectious diseases can be transmitted (passed) from one person to another.

3 Match up the beginnings and endings below to make complete sentences.

Beginnings

Natural barriers stop

Lysozyme is an enzyme

Acid in our stomach

If we cut ourselves

Endings

our blood clots to seal the wound.

that is found in tears.

kills microbes in our food.

microbes getting into our bodies.

4 How do disinfectants and antibiotics differ? Write down an example of each one.

5 Decide whether each statement is true or false. Write them in your book, correcting the ones that are false.

a If you are immune to a disease your white blood cells have forgotten how to fight it.

b A vaccine is an injection of weak or dead microbes, or bits of microbes.

c Babies can get some antibiotics from their mothers through the placenta.

6 An infectious disease called the Lurgy bug is sweeping the country. Lots of people are ill. The Government has asked to you to make a leaflet to explain how people can stop the Lurgy bug from spreading. Use the information below to help you.

o The Lurgy bug is caused by a type of bacteria.

o Like a cold, the Lurgy bug is spread through the air or when people touch.

o The Lurgy bug is killed at high temperatures. It is also killed by chlorine.

o People with the Lurgy bug can be cured if they take penicillin. What type of drug is penicillin? How does it work?

Ecological relationships

8D

What I should already know

- Different habitats have different conditions.

- Plants and animals are adapted to live in their habitats.

- How to draw food chains and food webs.

- Differences between members of the same species are called variation.

- Living things can be grouped by their features.

What I am going to meet in this unit

- Things that living organisms need to survive.

- How to classify green plants.

- How to collect data about a habitat.

- The communities in two habitats can be different.

- Living things in a community depend on each other.

- Pyramids of numbers.

Aaaaaaargh!

Hi! we've just moved in next door.

Predators can affect the number of prey animals in a habitat.

A **habitat** is a place where an organism lives. To live, an organism must be able to carry out the seven **life processes**. A habitat should provide animals with food, water and shelter. Plants need light (to make their food), water and space to grow.

The **conditions** in a habitat affect which organisms will live there. Plants and animals are **adapted** to their habitats. They have features that allow them to survive there. For example, camels are adapted to survive in the desert. Camels store water in their humps so they don't need to drink very often.

M	move
R	respire
S	(be) sensitive
G	grow
R	reproduce
E	excrete
N	nutrition

The seven life processes.

1 What are the seven life processes?

2 Unscramble these words:

   etherls   **ofod**   **atrew**   **gilth**

3 How is a squirrel adapted to survive in its habitat? Think about how it survives during the winter, and how it is able to climb trees.

Copy and complete using these words:

adapted   **survive**   **conditions**

The _____ in a habitat affect which organisms will live there. Plants and animals are _____ to their habitats. They have features that allow them to _____ there.

8D.2 Classifying plants

Living organisms can be **classified** (sorted into groups) by their **features**. The first step is to sort living organisms into two main groups, plants and animals. Animals can then be sorted into two smaller groups, **vertebrates** (animals with a backbone) and **invertebrates** (animals that don't have a backbone).

Plants can also be classified. The first step is to split them into two groups, those that produce **seeds** and those that produce **spores**. These two main groups can then be sorted into smaller groups:

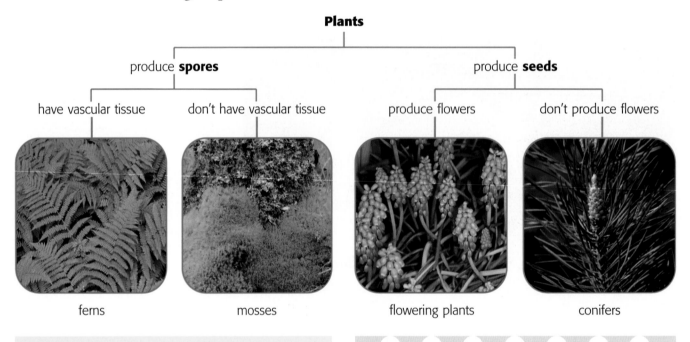

Plants

produce **spores**

have vascular tissue — ferns

don't have vascular tissue — mosses

produce **seeds**

produce flowers — flowering plants

don't produce flowers — conifers

1 What do we mean when we say that living things can be classified?

2 Unscramble these words:

bertavetres   deses   repsos

3 Use the diagram above to describe the main features of a fern. How do ferns and flowering plants differ? How do ferns and mosses differ?

Copy and complete using these words:

**spores   features   vertebrates
classified   seeds**

Living things can be _____ by their _____. Animals can be sorted into two main groups, _____ and invertebrates. Plants can also be sorted into two main groups, those that produce _____ and those that produce _____.

We can collect two types of data about a habitat.

Environmental conditions

The **conditions** in a habitat affect which organisms live there. Some organisms prefer to live somewhere that is damp and dark, whilst others prefer to live somewhere warm and sunny. We can use **ICT equipment** like lightmeters, temperature sensors and pH probes to measure environmental conditions.

Population size

A **population** is a group made up of one species in a habitat. We can **estimate** the size of a population of plants in a field by **sampling** with a **quadrat** (a 1 m square frame). The quadrat is thrown randomly onto the ground and the plants inside the square are counted. If we do this several times we can estimate the total number of plants on the field. The more times we do this, the more **accurate** our estimate will be.

1 What are the two types of data that we can collect about a habitat?

2 These words have had their vowels removed. What should they say?

tmprtr snsrs   lghtmtrs   pH prbs

3 How could you estimate the number of daisies on the school field? Remember that you must try to make your estimate as accurate as possible. How would you do this?

Copy and complete using these words:

**estimate   ICT   accurate
environmental   sampling**

The _____ conditions in a habitat affect which organisms will live there. We can use _____ equipment like pH probes and lightmeters to measure them. We can _____ the size of a population in a habitat by _____. The more samples we take, the more _____ our estimate will be.

Organisms depend on each other

The plants and animals that share a habitat are called a **community**. The **populations** (numbers) of the species in a community change all the time. They are affected by environmental factors like the availability of food.

A change in the population of one species can affect the other populations in a community. The hares in the food web eat grass. If there wasn't enough grass for the hares to eat, the number of hares would drop. This would affect the number of eagles, because eagles eat hares. The eagles might start eating more grouse and sheep, so the numbers of grouse and sheep would also change.

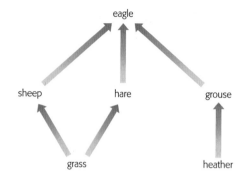

This food web shows the feeding relationships of animals and plants in a moorland habitat.

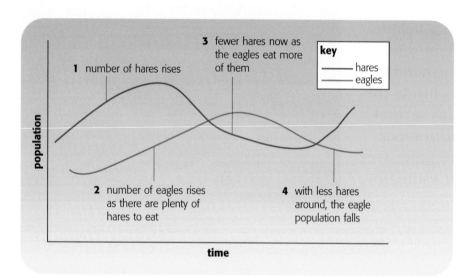

The populations of hares and eagles depend on each other.

1 **What do we call the plants and animals that share a habitat?**

2 **Unscramble these words:**

   liontopuap   tinymucmo

3 **Look at the food web above. Is heather a producer or a consumer? What would happen to the population of heather if the eagles started to eat more grouse? Explain your answer.**

Copy and complete using these words:

**environmental   species
community   populations   food**

The plants and animals that share a habitat are called a _____. The _____ in a community are affected by _____ factors like the availability of _____. A change in the population of one _____ can affect the other populations.

Pyramids of numbers

A **pyramid of numbers** shows us how the **populations** in a **food chain** are related. Like a food web, a pyramid of numbers always has the **producer** at the bottom. The **primary consumer** sits on top of the producer, with the **secondary consumer** above it. The lengths of the bars show the sizes of the populations.

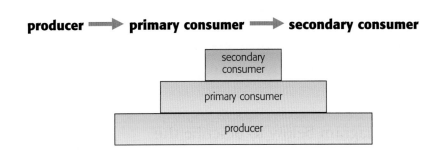

producer ➡ primary consumer ➡ secondary consumer

Often, when you go along a food chain the numbers get smaller and smaller. For example, hundreds of blades of grass might feed ten hares that are eaten by one eagle. Not all pyramids of numbers look like a pyramid though. Two blackbirds may eat lots of caterpillars that live on only one oak tree.

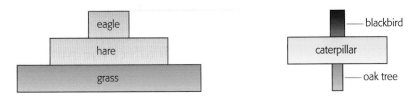

1 **What do pyramids of numbers show us?**

2 These words have had their vowels removed. What should they say?

prdcr   cnsmr   ppltns

3 Draw a pyramid of numbers for a food chain where heather is the producer, grouse eat the heather and an eagle eats the grouse. Remember to put the producer at the bottom of the pyramid.

Copy and complete using these words:

**populations   bottom   numbers
primary   chains   secondary**

Pyramids of _____ show us how the populations in food _____ are related. The producer is always at the _____ of the pyramid. The _____ consumer sits on top of the producer with the _____ consumer above it. The lengths of the bars show the sizes of the _____.

What have I learnt?

1 Name two different habitats. For each habitat, name an organism that lives there and describe how it is adapted to survive.

2 Use the diagram below to describe the features of a moss.

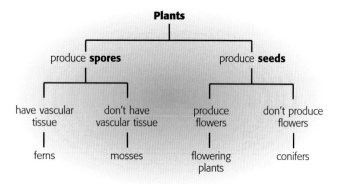

3 What is a quadrat? How could you use a quadrat to estimate the number of daffodils that are in a garden?

4 Match up the beginnings and endings below to make complete sentences.

Beginnings

The organisms that share a habitat

The populations in a habitat

Populations are affected by

The number of a group made up of one species in a habitat

Endings

change all the time.

are called a community.

is called a population.

environmental factors.

5 Not all pyramids of numbers look like a pyramid. Draw a pyramid of numbers for the food chain below and explain why it doesn't look like a pyramid.

rose bush ⟶ **aphids** ⟶ **ladybird**

6 Your local council wants to build some new houses in a meadow near where you live. There is a population of owls in your area. They eat fieldmice that live in the meadow. You think that the number of owls will drop if the new houses are built in the meadow.

- Write a letter to the council explaining why you think the number of owls will drop.

- Explain how a drop in the number of fieldmice will affect the number of owls.

- Include a food chain and a pyramid of numbers to support your argument.

Atoms and elements

What I should already know

- How solids, liquids and gases differ.
- All materials are made up of particles.
- How the particles in solids, liquids and gases are arranged.
- Substances can either be pure or a mixture.

What I am going to meet in this unit

- Different materials are made by joining different elements together.
- The names and symbols of some elements.
- The periodic table.
- How elements and compounds are different.
- Compounds are made by chemical reactions.
- How to write a formula for a compound.

I'm in my element!

The objects in the picture are made from different **materials**. All of them are made from **elements**.

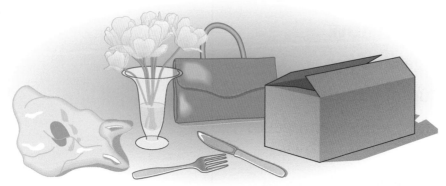

These objects are made from different materials.

Elements are substances that are made up of only one type of particle. There are only about 100 different elements, but they can join together in different ways to make millions of different materials. We can think of elements as being like the ingredients in a recipe. For example, flour can be used to make lots of different foods. In a similar way, an element like carbon can be used to make lots of different materials. The different elements that make up a material determine its **properties**.

Like an element, flour can be used to make lots of different things.

1 What is an element?
2 These words have had their vowels removed. What should they say?

   lmnts   prprts   mtrls

3 Try to explain why we can think of flour as being like an element. Give some examples of foods that contain flour.

Copy and complete using these words:

**properties   elements   join
materials   100**

There are millions of different _____.
They are all made from _____. There are only about _____ different elements, but they can _____ together in different ways to produce materials with different _____.

Elements are substances that are made from only one type of particle. The particles that make up elements are called **atoms**. Atoms are the building blocks of elements.

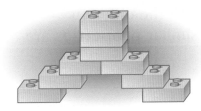

This tower is like an element. All of the blocks that have been used to build it are the same.

Each element is made from only one kind of atom. For example, iron is an element that is made up of iron atoms. All of the atoms in iron are the same.

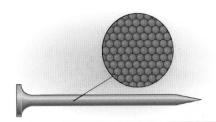

This iron nail is made up of iron atoms.

Each element has a **symbol** of one or two letters. The first letter is always a capital letter and the second letter is always a small letter. These symbols are the same all over the world.

Element	Symbol
Hydrogen	H
Oxygen	O
Carbon	C
Copper	Cu

1 What is an atom?

2 Unscramble these words:

　stoma　**emtsenel**　**mobsly**

3 Helium is an element that is usually a gas. Draw a particle diagram to show how the atoms in helium are arranged. Are all of the atoms the same?

Copy and complete using these words:

particles　　**atoms**　　**symbol**
O　　　**elements**

_____ are substances that are made from _____ called _____. Each element is made up only one kind of atom and has a _____. The symbol for oxygen is _____.

The **periodic table** is a table of all the different **elements**. Elements that have similar **properties** are grouped together in columns.

H																	He
Li	Be											B	C	N	O	F	Ne
Na	Mg											Al	Si	P	S	Cl	Ar
K	Ca	Sc	Ti	V	Cr	Mn	Fe	Co	Ni	Cu	Zn	Ga	Ge	As	Se	Br	Kr
Rb	Sr	Y	Zr	Nb	Mo	Tc	Ru	Rh	Pd	Ag	Cd	In	Sn	Sb	Te	I	Xe
Cs	Ba	La	Hf	Ta	W	Re	Os	Ir	Pt	Au	Hg	Tl	Pb	Bi	Po	At	Rn
Fr	Ra																

Key

☐ metals ☐ non-metals

The elements that are **metals** are grouped on the left-hand side of the periodic table (in blue). All of the metals are solids at room temperature, except for mercury which is a liquid.

The elements that are **non-metals** are grouped on the right-hand side of the periodic table (in red). These are all gases or solids at room temperature, except for bromine which is a liquid.

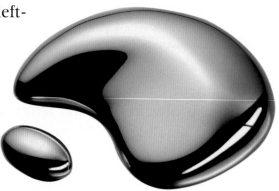

Mercury is a liquid at room temperature.

1 What is the periodic table?

2 Unscramble these words:

  sleenemt   ideripoc   almste

3 Na is the symbol for sodium. Write down the symbols of the five elements that have similar properties to sodium. How are these elements grouped together in the periodic table?

Copy and complete using these words:

**properties   non-metals   periodic
metals   elements**

The _____ table is a table of all the different _____. Elements with similar _____ are grouped together. Elements that are _____ are on the left-hand side. Elements that are _____ are on the right-hand side.

Particles that are made from more than one atom are called **molecules**. For example, oxygen molecules are made from two oxygen atoms. When we want to describe an oxygen molecule, we write the **formula** O_2. The small number tells us how many atoms of oxygen there are.

An oxygen molecule is made up of two oxygen atoms.

Compounds are substances that are made from more than one element. Compounds are made by chemical reactions. The atoms are chemically joined.

The formula of a compound tells us which elements its molecules are made from, and in what ratio. For example, the formula for water is H_2O. There are two capital letters in the formula so we know that there are two different elements; hydrogen and oxygen. We also know that there are two hydrogen atoms for every oxygen atom.

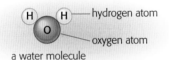

a water molecule

Water is a compound. Water molecules are made up of two hydrogen atoms and one oxygen atom.

1 What is a molecule?

2 These words have had their vowels removed. What should they say?

   mlcl   frml   cmpnd

3 The formula for carbon dioxide is CO_2. Which elements make up carbon dioxide? How many atoms of each element make up a carbon dioxide molecule?

Copy and complete using these words:

**element   compounds   formula
molecules   atoms**

Particles that are made from more than one atom are called _____. _____ are made from more than one _____. Their _____ are chemically joined up. The _____ of a compound tells us what elements its molecules are made from.

Compounds are made by **chemical reactions**. Chemical reactions can also make compounds change into other compounds. We can write **word equations** to tell us what happens in chemical reactions.

Word equations always have the **reactants** (the substances that you start with) on the left. The substances that are made by the reaction go on the right. These are the **products**. The arrow means 'changes into', and points to the products.

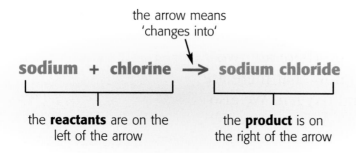

the arrow means 'changes into'

sodium + chlorine → sodium chloride

the **reactants** are on the left of the arrow

the **product** is on the right of the arrow

Common salt is a compound called sodium chloride.

The word equation above shows how the elements sodium and chlorine react to form a compound called sodium chloride. When compounds form from two or more elements, their name usually ends with 'ide'.

1 How are compounds made?

2 Unscramble these words:

tactranes   soctpurd   utoqiaen

3 Write a word equation to describe the chemical reaction that happens when magnesium and oxygen react to produce magnesium oxide.

Copy and complete using these words:

**reactants   equations   products
reactions   right**

Word _____ tell us what happens in chemical _____. The _____ are always on the left, and the products are always on the right. The arrow always points towards the _____.

What have I learnt?

1 How many different types of atoms make up an element?

2 Copy and complete the table below to show some elements and their symbols.

Element	Symbol
Hydrogen	
	O
Carbon	
	Na
Magnesium	

3 Look at the periodic table on page 38. Which of the element symbols below describe elements that are non-metals?

H   N   F   Mg   Al   Cl

4 Match up the beginnings and endings below to make complete sentences.

Beginnings

Molecules are made from

Compounds are made from

Water (H_2O) is a compound made from

Sodium chloride (NaCl) is a compound made from

Endings

two hydrogen atoms and one oxygen atom.

more than one element.

one sodium atom and one chlorine atom.

more than one atom.

5 Write a word equation to describe what happens when potassium and chlorine react together. What is the product of the reaction?

6 Design a poster to help next year's Year 8 students with this unit. It should be colourful and explain what each of the following are:

o Atoms
o Elements
o Molecules
o Compounds

Compounds and mixtures

What I should already know

- All materials are made up of particles.
- A chemical reaction is a change that can't be turned back easily.
- How elements and compounds differ.
- The names and symbols of some elements.
- Mixtures are made from more than one substance, and can be separated easily.

What I am going to meet in this unit

- We can use formulae to describe compounds.
- Compounds have different properties to the elements that they are made from.
- In a compound the elements are chemically joined.
- In a mixture the substances are not chemically joined.
- Pure elements and compounds have fixed melting and boiling points.

Can you see your carbon dioxide molecule here sir?

I don't know. They all look the same!

LOST PROPERTY

CO_2 MOLECULES

Elements are made from only one kind of **atom**, and can't be broken down into anything simpler.
Compounds are made from the atoms of two or more different elements. Their atoms are chemically joined together. They can only be broken down into their separate elements by a chemical reaction.

We can write a **formula** to describe how a compound is made up. The formula tells us which elements the compound is made from, and in what **ratio** (how many atoms of each element there are). For each compound, the ratio of elements that make it up is fixed (always the same).

oxygen atoms

carbon atom

A carbon dioxide molecule.

C is the symbol for carbon.

CO_2

The little '2' means that there are two oxygens.

O is the symbol for oxygen.

The formula for carbon dioxide tell us that carbon dioxide molecules are always made up of two oxygen atoms and a carbon atom.

1 What are compounds made from?

2 Unscramble these words:

mota   romaluf   otiar

3 Which of the following are element symbols, and which are formulas of compounds? How can you tell?

NaCl   Cu   Mg H_2O
$CuCO_3$ O

Copy and complete using these words:

chemically   compounds   formula
ratio   elements

_____ are made from the atoms of two or more different _____, _____ joined together. The _____ of a compound tells us which elements the compound is made from, and in what _____.

When two or more **elements** react to make **compounds**, their atoms join together. New substances are made. The **chemical properties** of these new substances are different to those of the elements that formed them.

Iron and sulphur are the reactants.

Iron and sulphur are both elements. When they are heated, they react to make a compound called iron sulphide. We know that a chemical reaction is happening because the reactants glow. The chemical properties of iron sulphide (the product) are very different to those of the reactants, iron and sulphur. Iron sulphide looks different to iron and sulphur, and is not magnetic like iron.

Iron sulphide is the product.

iron
(symbol **Fe**)

sulphur
(symbol **S**)

iron sulphide
(formula **FeS**)

When iron and sulphur react to form iron sulphide, their atoms become chemically joined. The formula for iron sulphide is FeS. This tells us that there is one atom of iron for every atom of sulphur.

1 Is iron sulphide an element or a compound?

2 These words have had their vowels removed. What should they say?

prprts   **slphr**   **rctn**

3 How do the chemical properties of iron sulphide differ from those of iron and sulphur?

Copy and complete using these words:

compound   **atoms**   **chemical**
properties   **elements**

When two or more _____ react to form a _____, their _____ join together in new ways. The _____ _____ of the compound are different to those of the elements that it is made from.

Reacting compounds

When two or more **elements** react together they form new substances called **compounds**. Compounds can also take part in **chemical reactions**.

The diagram on the right lists some of the signs that can tell us that a chemical reaction is taking place. We can only say that a chemical reaction has happened if we see a change that can't be turned back easily.

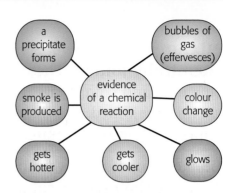

a precipitate forms — bubbles of gas (effervesces) — evidence of a chemical reaction — smoke is produced — colour change — gets hotter — gets cooler — glows

If you heat green copper carbonate it changes colour because a chemical reaction happens. Black copper oxide and carbon dioxide gas are produced.

copper carbonate ⟶ copper oxide + carbon dioxide

Silver nitrate solution and sodium chloride solution are both clear and colourless. When they react, a white precipitate (solid) forms and sinks to the bottom of the test tube.

silver nitrate + sodium chloride ⟶ silver chloride + sodium nitrate

1 Name three signs that can tell us that a chemical reaction is happening.

2 Unscramble these words:

   tipetapierc   **tiecraon**

3 What do we call an insoluble solid that forms when two solutions react together?

Copy and complete using these words:

**colour   compounds   elements
precipitate**

Both _____ and _____ can take part in chemical reactions. Signs like a change in _____, or a _____ forming, tell us that a chemical reaction has taken place.

Mixtures contain two or more substances that are not **chemically joined**. They can be made from both elements and compounds. Because they are not chemically joined, the different substances that make up a mixture can be separated easily.

Unlike compounds, we can't write a formula for a mixture. The **ratio** of substances that make up a mixture isn't fixed. Air is a mixture that contains the elements nitrogen, oxygen and argon. It also contains the compounds water and carbon dioxide. The amount of each substance in air can vary. For example, the air that you breathe out has less oxygen in it than the air that you breathe in. It also contains more carbon dioxide.

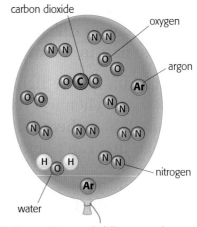

Air is a mixture of different substances.

	Percentage in air breathed in	Percentage in air breathed out
oxygen	21	17
nitrogen	78	78
carbon dioxide	0.04	4
other gases	0.96	0.96
water	variable	saturated

1 What is a mixture?

2 Name one compound and two elements that are found in air.

3 Air is a mixture. Think of another example of a mixture, and try to name the different substances that make it up. Which of them are compounds and which are elements?

Copy and complete using these words:

substances   air   ratio
mixture   formula

A _____ contains two or more _____ that are not chemically joined. We can't write a _____ for a mixture because the _____ of the substances that make it up is not fixed. _____ is a mixture.

Melting points and boiling points

The **melting point** of a substance is the temperature at which it **changes state** from a solid to a liquid. The **boiling point** of a substance is the temperature at which it changes state from a liquid to a gas.

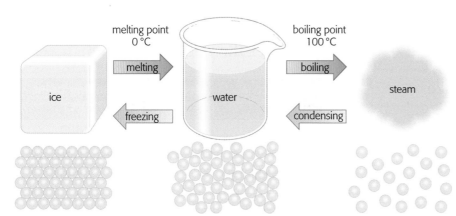

The melting point of water is 0 °C. At this temperature, icicles will start to melt.

A **pure** element or compound will always melt and boil at the same temperature. Its melting point and boiling point are fixed. If a substance is **impure** (a mixture) its melting point and boiling point change. For example, the boiling point of pure water is 100 °C, but the boiling point of salty water is around 102 °C. We can test a substance to see if it is pure, if we know what its melting and boiling points are.

1 What is the melting point of a substance?

2 Unscramble these words:

   muepir   igbinol   limgnet

3 The boiling point of pure water is 100 ˚C and its melting point is 0 ˚C. How could you test tap water to see if it is pure?

Copy and complete using these words:

**impure   melting   points
pure   fixed   boiling**

Pure substances have _____ melting and boiling _____. If a substance is _____, its melting point and _____ point change. We can test a substance to see if it is _____, if we know what its _____ and boiling points are.

1 What is the formula for carbon dioxide? Is carbon dioxide an element or a compound? How can you tell?

2 Match up the beginnings and endings below to make complete sentences.

Beginnings

Iron and sulphur react to make

Compounds are made when

The formula for iron sulphide

The chemical properties of iron sulphide

Endings

are different to those of iron and sulphur.

two or more elements react.

is FeS.

a compound called iron sulphide.

3 Magnesium chloride and hydrogen gas are produced when magnesium reacts with hydrochloric acid. Write a word equation for this reaction.

4 Match up each picture with the correct label.

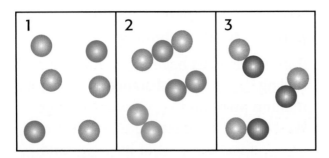

a A pure compound.
b A mixture of elements.
c A mixture of two elements and a compound.

5 Use the information in the table to answer the questions below:

Substance	Melting point (°C)	Boiling point (°C)
calcium	840	1480
chlorine	-101	-35
calcium chloride	780	1590

a Which substance has the lowest melting point?
b Which substance has the highest melting point?
c Is chlorine a solid, a liquid or a gas at 25 °C?

6 Make a list of the ten most important words from this unit. Write a clue for each one, and then use your clues to make a 'compounds and mixtures' crossword.

Rocks and weathering

What I should already know

- Different rocks have different properties.
- Soil forms from rocks.
- About acids, alkalis and the pH scale.
- How the particles in solids, liquids and gases are arranged.
- When water evaporates from a solution of salty water, solid salt is left behind.

What I am going to meet in this unit

- Rocks are made up of different minerals.
- Different rocks have different textures. Some are porous, others are non-porous.
- Rocks can be weathered by physical, chemical and biological processes.
- Weathered pieces of rock can be transported somewhere else. They may then make new rocks.
- How sedimentary rocks are formed.

You look rough.

I know. It's really eroding my confidence.

Rocks are mixtures of **minerals** (solid substances that make up the Earth's crust). There are lots of different types of rock. Each type is made up of a different mixture of minerals.

Different rocks have different **properties**, like colour, hardness and **texture** (how they look and feel). The texture of a rock depends on how its **grains** (mineral particles) are arranged. Some rocks are **porous**. There are little spaces between the grains that water can get into. Other rocks are **non-porous**. Their grains **interlock** (fit closely together) and there are no spaces between them for water to get into.

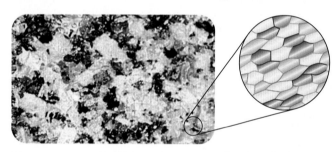

Non-porous rocks like granite are very hard and often look shiny. Their grains have formed interlocking crystals.

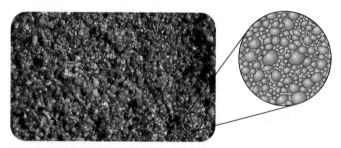

Porous rocks like sandstone are usually dull and crumbly. Their grains do not interlock. There are spaces between them that water can get into.

1 What are rocks?

2 Unscramble these words:

   rilnames   uxetret   osrupo

3 Draw a picture to show how the grains are arranged in a porous rock. Draw another picture to show how the grains are arranged in a non-porous rock. How do they differ?

Copy and complete using these words:

properties   minerals   porous
grains   interlock   texture

Rocks are mixtures of _____. Different rocks have different _____. The _____ of a rock depends on how its _____ are arranged. Water can get into spaces between the grains in _____ rocks because they do not _____.

What is weathering?

Over time, rocks are **weathered**. They are slowly broken down into smaller pieces. There are three types of weathering: **physical**, **biological** and **chemical**.

Physical weathering
This is caused by changes in the temperature of the environment.

Biological weathering
This is caused by plants and animals. The roots of plants can get into cracks in rocks. As they grow, the cracks get bigger until a piece of the rock breaks off. Digging animals can also make cracks in rocks get bigger.

Biological weathering is caused by plants and animals.

Chemical weathering
This is caused by chemical reactions. Rainwater is naturally acidic and can wear rocks away over time. Air pollution makes rainwater more acidic than normal rain. This **acid rain** wears rocks away even more quickly.

This gravestone is made of limestone. It has been worn away by chemical weathering.

1 What happens when rocks are weathered?

2 These words have had their vowels removed. What should they say?

blgcl   chmcl   physcl

3 Write a sentence to explain how biological weathering is caused. Do the same for physical and chemical weathering.

Copy and complete using these words:

**biological   physical   weathered
temperature   chemical**

When rocks are _____ they are slowly broken down into smaller pieces. _____ weathering is caused by chemical reactions. _____ weathering is caused by changes in _____. _____ weathering is caused by plants and animals.

The temperature of the environment changes from day to night. These temperature changes cause **physical weathering**. There are two types of physical weathering: **freeze-thaw** and **onion skin**.

Freeze-thaw weathering

Water **expands** (gets bigger) when it freezes. If it freezes when it is in a crack in a rock, it will make the crack get bigger. If water freezes and thaws (melts) in a crack many times, the crack will get even larger. Eventually the rock breaks up.

Freeze-thaw weathering makes the cracks in a rock get bigger and bigger.

Onion skin weathering (exfoliation)

Rocks expand during the day because they are heated by the Sun, and contract during the night when it is cooler. If this happens many times, the surface of the rock may begin to peel away like the skin of an onion.

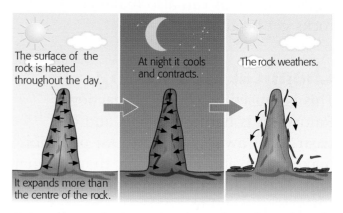

Onion skin weathering makes the surface of a rock peel away.

1 What are the two types of physical weathering?

2 Unscramble these words:

inono   **rezfee-what**   **gnahewiter**

3 Onion skin weathering is caused by rocks expanding and contracting. Explain why rocks expand when they get hot (think back to what you learnt about particles in Year 7).

Copy and complete using these words:

heated   temperature   freeze-thaw onion skin   physical weathering

Changes in _____ cause _____ _____. _____ weathering is caused by water freezing and expanding. _____ _____ weathering happens when the surface of a rock is _____ and cooled many times.

Weathering causes rocks to break up into **fragments** (smaller pieces). These fragments can be **transported** (carried away) by water or by the wind, and **deposited** (dropped) somewhere else. When this happens, we say that the rocks have been **eroded**. The rock fragments are called **sediment**.

Rock fragments can be different sizes. It takes more energy for a river to move larger fragments than smaller ones, so large fragments are not transported very far. They are deposited upstream, where the river has lots of energy. Smaller fragments like pebbles, sand and silt are deposited downstream. The smaller the fragments, the further they are transported. They will also be rounder and smoother.

Large fragments are deposited upstream where the river has lots of energy.

The river has less energy because it is wider and flatter. Smaller fragments are deposited here.

Fine sediment like sand and silt is deposited here, where the river has the least energy.

1 What happens to a rock when it is eroded?

2 These words have had their vowels removed. What should they say?

sdmnt   trnsprtd   dpstd

3 Would you expect to find smooth round pebbles upstream or downstream of a river? Explain your answer.

Copy and complete using these words:

sediment   transported   deposited weathered   eroded

When a rock is _____ and the rock fragments are _____ to other places, we say that it has been _____. The fragments are called _____, and can be transported by water or wind before being _____.

Sedimentary rocks form from layers of deposited sediment:

Some sedimentary rocks form when new layers of sediment are deposited on top of older layers. This process is called **accumulation**. Sometimes dead plants or animals get buried in the sediment and form **fossils**. The layers of sediment then fix together in a process known as **consolidation**. Finally, minerals that were dissolved in the water come out of solution and stick the sediment grains together. This is called **cementation**.

These ammonite fossils were once ancient sea creatures.

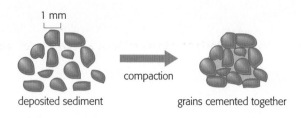

1 mm

deposited sediment → compaction → grains cemented together

Other sedimentary rocks form when water evaporates. Minerals that were dissolved in the water are deposited and form rocks called **evaporites**. Gypsum is an example of a sedimentary rock that forms in this way.

1 What happens to grains of sedmiment during cementation?

2 Unscramble these words:

luacmonautic   ildoncaoniost

3 Imagine that you are looking at a cliff. Are the oldest rocks at the top of the cliff or the bottom? Explain your answer using these words:

sediment   deposited accumulation

Copy and complete using these words:

sediment   fossils   sedimentary buried   evaporates

Some _____ rocks form when new layers of _____ are deposited on top of older layers. Others form when water _____, leaving minerals behind. _____ form when dead plants or animals get _____ by sediment.

What have I learnt?

1 What do we mean when we say that a rock is porous? Give an example of a porous rock.

2 Match up the beginnings and endings below to make complete sentences.

Beginnings

When rocks are weathered they are

The three types of weathering are

Chemical weathering is caused by

Biological weathering is caused by

Endings

plants and animals.

broken down into smaller pieces.

biological, chemical and physical.

chemical reactions.

3 What happens when rocks are weathered by freeze-thaw weathering?

4 Write the sentences below in the correct order:

o Large fragments are deposited upstream.

o The sediment can then be transported by water and deposited somewhere else.

o Smaller fragments move further downstream before they are deposited, becoming smoother and rounder.

o Weathering breaks rocks up into fragments called sediment.

5 Answer the questions below.

a What happens during accumulation?

b What happens during consolidation?

c What happens during cementation?

6 A fossil of a *Tyrannosaurus rex* has just been found in Devon. You have been asked to write an article about it for a newspaper. Include the following information in your article:

o Where was the fossil found?

o What type of rock was the fossil found in?

o How was this rock formed?

o How did the fossil form in the rock?

o Does the fossil look scary?

The rock cycle

What I should already know

- Different rocks have different properties.
- Rocks can be weathered.
- Weathered pieces of rock can be transported and deposited somewhere else.
- How sedimentary rocks are formed.

What I am going to meet in this unit

- The three types of rock and their different characteristics.
- Sedimentary rocks are formed from deposits of sediment.
- Igneous rocks are formed when molten rock cools and solidifies.
- Metamorphic rocks are formed when rocks are changed by heat and pressure.
- The rock cycle.

I'm baking a marble cake!

Why is there a piece of limestone in the oven?

Rocks can be sorted into groups by their characteristics, just like living organisms. There are three main types of rock: **igneous**, **metamorphic** and **sedimentary**. They are formed in different ways and have different properties.

This metamorphic rock has wavy bands.

The grains in this sedimentary sandstone are cemented together.

Rock Type	Sedimentary	Igneous	Metamorphic
Structure	form in layers, grains are cemented together, can be crumbly	crystals interlock and are randomly arranged	often look 'sugary', particles may form wavy bands or be randomly arranged
Are there fossils?	usually	no	sometimes there are remains of fossils, but it's rare
Porosity	often porous	non-porous	varies, usually less porous than sedimentary rocks
Examples	sandstone and limestone	basalt and granite	slate and marble

1 What are the three main types of rock called?

2 Unscramble these words:

   soupro   **rayugs**   **ronkcielt**

3 How are igneous rocks different to metamorphic rocks? Use the information in the table above.

Copy and complete using these words:

sedimentary   **properties**   **igneous**
porosity   **metamorphic**

There are three main types of rock: _____, _____ and _____. They are formed in different ways and have different _____, like their structure and _____.

8H.2 Sedimentary rocks

Sedimentary rocks form from deposits of sediment. They have grainy textures, are usually **porous** and often contain **fossils** of dead plants or animals. They can be formed in three different ways:

o when layers of sediment from weathered rocks are cemented together

o when water evaporates and layers of minerals are left behind

o from the remains of living organisms.

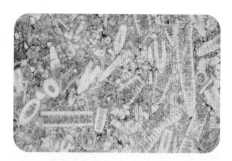

This crinoidal limestone formed when the remains of ancient sea creatures were cemented together.

Sedimentary rocks usually form in layers called **beds**. As different layers build up on top of each other, they are **compacted** together. The pressure causes minerals that are dissolved in water to come out of solution. These minerals **cement** (stick) the grains together.

You can see different beds of sedimentary rock in this picture of the Grand Canyon.

1 Sedimentary rocks can form in three different ways. What are they?

2 These words have had their vowels removed. What should they say?

cmntd   fssls   bds

3 In Unit 8G you learnt about rocks and weathering. Use your knowledge to explain what fossils are and how they are formed.

Copy and complete using these words:

**fossils   deposits   cement
pressure   beds   minerals**

Sedimentary rocks form from _____ of sediment. They are usually formed in layers called _____, and often contain _____. As layers build up, the _____ causes _____ to come out of solution and _____ the grains together.

The word **igneous** comes from the Latin word for 'fire'. Igneous rocks form when **magma** (hot molten rock) cools and solidifies. They are non-porous because they have interlocking crystals, and don't contain fossils.

The size of the crystals in an igneous rock depends on how slowly the magma cooled. **Intrusive** igneous rocks form when magma cools under the Earth's surface. Their crystals are large because they have a long time to grow. If magma reaches the Earth's surface it is called **lava**. Lava cools quickly to form **extrusive** igneous rocks. These look glassy or have very small crystals because the crystals don't have much time to grow.

Granite forms when magma cools slowly under the Earth's surface. The crystals are large because they have a long time to grow.

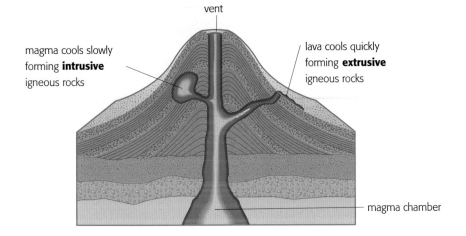

vent

magma cools slowly forming **intrusive** igneous rocks

lava cools quickly forming **extrusive** igneous rocks

magma chamber

Obsidian looks glassy. It forms when lava cools very quickly on the Earth's surface.

1 What is magma?

2 Unscramble these words:

usitviren   tisxuveer   vaal

3 Answer these questions:

a Is granite an intrusive or an extrusive igneous rock? Explain your answer.

b Why don't igneous rocks like granite contain fossils?

Copy and complete using these words:

intrusive   slower   extrusive
magma   larger

Igneous rocks form when _____ cools and solidifies. The _____ the magma cools the _____ the crystals. _____ igneous rocks form when magma cools under the Earth's surface. _____ igneous rocks form on the Earth's surface.

The word **metamorphic** means 'changing form'. Metamorphic rocks form when rocks are changed by **heat** and **pressure**. They are often sugary and can have wavy bands. Examples are:

o marble (forms from limestone)

o slate (forms from shale)

o metaquartzite (forms from sandstone).

Sometimes magma (molten rock) forces its way into cracks in rocks under the Earth's surface. This is called an **igneous intrusion**. The magma is so hot (over 1000 °C) that the rocks around the intrusion are baked and changed into metamorphic rocks.

When limestone is heated at low pressure …

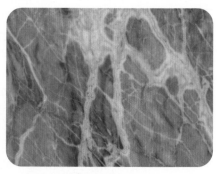

… it changes into marble!

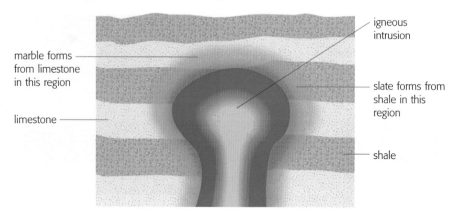

igneous intrusion

marble forms from limestone in this region

limestone

slate forms from shale in this region

shale

1 What does the word 'metamorphic' mean?

2 These words have had their vowels removed. What should they say?

   mrbl   **mtqrtzt**   **slt**

3 How do metamorphic rocks form? Include these words in your answer:

   heat   **pressure**   **igneous intrusion**

Copy and complete using these words:

intrusion   **heat**   **sugary**
metamorphic   **pressure**

_____ rocks form when rocks are changed by _____ and _____. They form when the rocks around an igneous _____ are baked and changed. They are often _____ and can have wavy bands.

The surface of the Earth changes all the time. Over many years, old rocks are recycled into new rocks. This process is called the **rock cycle**. The rock cycle links together the processes that form and change the three types of rock: igneous, sedimentary and metamorphic.

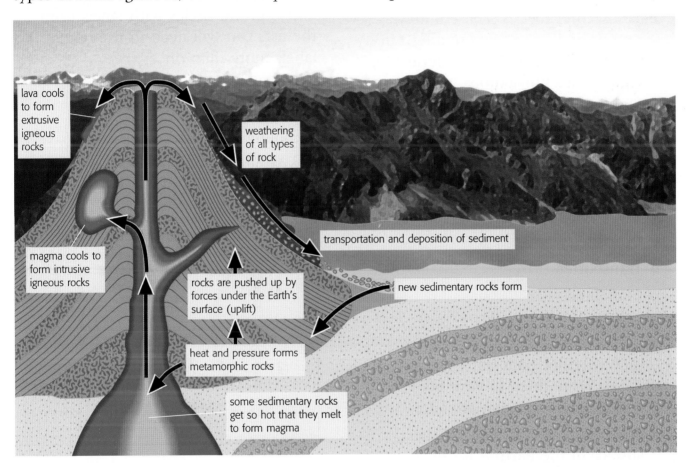

lava cools to form extrusive igneous rocks

weathering of all types of rock

magma cools to form intrusive igneous rocks

transportation and deposition of sediment

rocks are pushed up by forces under the Earth's surface (uplift)

new sedimentary rocks form

heat and pressure forms metamorphic rocks

some sedimentary rocks get so hot that they melt to form magma

1 What do we call the process by which old rocks are recycled into new ones?

2 Unscramble these words:

tengmil   harinweteg   fulpit

3 Rocks on the Earth's surface are always being weathered. Why hasn't the Earth's surface been worn away until it is completely flat?

Copy and complete using these words:

**metamorphic   rock cycle
sedimentary   surface**

The Earth's _____ changes all the time. Old rocks are recycled into new rocks by the _____ _____. This links together the processes that form and change _____, igneous and _____ rocks.

What have I learnt?

1 Peter has found three rocks. Decide whether each rock is igneous, metamorphic or sedimentary.

  a The first rock is a little bit porous. It looks sugary.

  b The second rock is a bit crumbly, porous and has a fossil of a fern in it.

  c The third rock has large interlocking crystals. It's non-porous, and there aren't any fossils in it.

2 Write the keywords below in the correct order, to show how some sedimentary rocks are formed.

  o Compaction

  o Deposited

  o Transported

  o Cemented

  o Weathered

3 Decide whether each statement is true or false. Write them in your book, correcting the ones that are false.

  a When molten rock reaches the surface of the Earth it is called magma.

  b Intrusive igneous rocks form when magma cools quickly under the Earth's surface.

  c Extrusive igneous rocks form when lava cools quickly on the surface of the Earth.

  d Igneous rocks always contain fossils.

4 What is the name of the rock that can be changed into marble by heat and pressure?

5 Copy the flow chart below. Replace the letters in the circles with labels from the list. You will need to use one of the labels more than once.

  o melting

  o heat and pressure

  o cooling

  o weathering

  o cementation

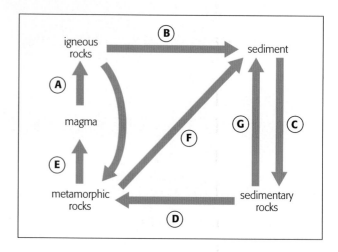

6 Draw a cartoon strip to explain how the three different types of rock are formed. Try to name two examples of each rock type.

Heating and cooling

What I should already know

○ How to use a thermometer to measure temperature.

○ How to keep substances warm or cold.

○ Some materials conduct heat well.

○ How the arrangement of particles in a solid, liquid or gas changes during a change of state.

What I am going to meet in this unit

○ Temperature can be measured in degrees Celsius (°C).

○ Thermal energy (heat) is transferred when something gets hotter or colder.

○ Thermal conductors conduct heat well.

○ Thermal insulators do not conduct heat well.

○ Solids are good thermal conductors, liquids and gases are not.

○ Solids, liquids and gases expand when they are heated and contract when they are cooled.

○ Melting points and boiling points.

I think we've just found her melting point!

Temperature is a measure of how hot or cold something is. Temperature is not the same as heat. Heat is a type of energy called **thermal energy**. Like other types of energy, thermal energy is measured in **joules (J)**.

If we want to measure the temperature of something we use a **thermometer**. Thermometers usually measure temperature in **degrees Celsius (°C)**. The Celsius temperature scale is based on two fixed points: the melting point of water (0 °C) and the boiling point of water (100 °C). The human body has a temperature of 37 °C. Absolute zero (-273 °C) is the coldest temperature possible.

To read a thermometer accurately we must hold it at eye level. If we look down on it, or up to it, the reading will be wrong.

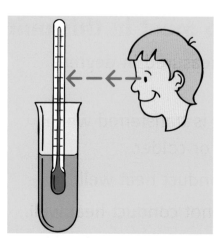

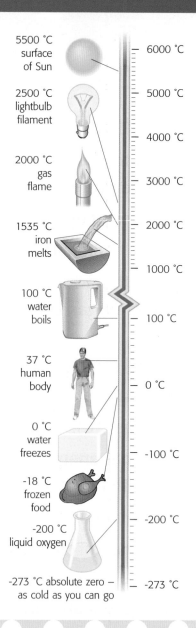

5500 °C surface of Sun — 6000 °C

2500 °C lightbulb filament — 5000 °C

— 4000 °C

2000 °C gas flame — 3000 °C

1535 °C iron melts — 2000 °C

— 1000 °C

100 °C water boils — 100 °C

37 °C human body — 0 °C

0 °C water freezes — -100 °C

-18 °C frozen food

-200 °C liquid oxygen — -200 °C

-273 °C absolute zero – as cold as you can go — -273 °C

---

1 What do we use if we want to measure the temperature of something?

2 Unscramble these words:

retmehmrote   seucils   maretuteper

3 Heat and temperature are not the same. Write a sentence to describe what temperature is. How is it measured? Do the same for heat.

Copy and complete using these words:

**Celsius   thermal   thermometer
temperature   joules**

_____ is a measure of how hot or cold something is. It is usually measured in degrees _____ (°C). We can measure temperature using a _____. Heat is a type of energy called _____ energy. It is measured in _____ (J).

When things get hotter or colder **thermal energy** (heat) is **transferred**. Things get hotter when thermal energy flows towards them, and colder when thermal energy flows away from them.

If two things are different temperatures, thermal energy will flow from the hotter one to the colder one. When we heat a pan of soup on a gas cooker, the flame is hotter than the soup. Thermal energy flows from the flame to the soup and the soup gets hotter. When we stop heating the soup it begins to cool. The soup is hotter than the air around it. Thermal energy flows from the soup to the air and the soup gets colder.

When you stand near a bonfire you can feel the thermal energy that is being transferred.

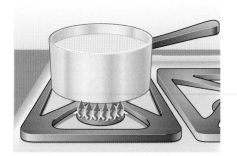

Here, thermal energy flows from the flame to the soup. This is because the soup is cooler than the flame.

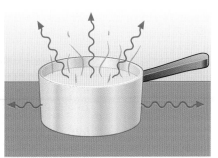

The soup cools because thermal energy flows from the soup to the air around it. The air is cooler than the soup.

1 What happens when things get hotter or colder?

2 These words have had their vowels removed. What should they say?

thrml nrgy   **cndctrs**

3 When you take ice cream out of the freezer does thermal energy flow from the ice cream to the air around it, or from the air to the ice cream? Explain your answer.

Copy and complete using these words:

towards   **temperatures**   **cooler**
hotter   **transferred**   **away**

Thermal energy is _____ when things get hotter or colder. Things get hotter when thermal energy flows _____ them, and colder when it flows _____ from them. If two things are different _____, thermal energy will flow from the _____ one to the _____ one.

Thermal energy (heat) travels through solids by **conduction**. We say that materials that conduct heat well are good **thermal conductors**. Metals are good thermal conductors. Materials that do not conduct heat well are called **thermal insulators**. Wood and some plastics are good thermal insulators.

One of the ways that we can save energy is by insulating our homes. Some examples of insulation methods are shown in the table below. Stopping heat escaping from our homes doesn't just help us save non-renewable energy resources like fossil fuels. It costs us less to heat our homes, and also helps to reduce air pollution.

This pan is made from a metal that is a good thermal conductor. The handle is made from a plastic that is a good thermal insulator. It stops you from burning yourself when you pick up the pan.

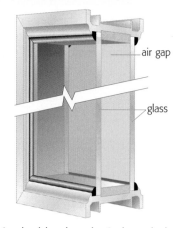

air gap

glass

The air gap in double glazed windows helps to stop heat escaping.

Insulation method	Money saved per year (£)
loft insulation (installing from scratch)	157
loft insulation (making it thicker)	40
double glazing	34
cavity wall insulation	70
draught excluders	8
lagging hot water tank	11

1 How does heat energy travel through solids?

2 Unscramble these words:

turncocod   sailornut

3 When you buy fish and chips from a chip shop they are wrapped in paper. Use the words below to explain why they are wrapped in paper:

heat   transferred
thermal insulator

Copy and complete using these words:

conductors   insulating   pollution
conduction   insulators

Thermal energy travels through solids by _____. Materials that conduct heat well are good thermal _____. Those that don't are good thermal _____. _____ our homes helps us to save energy, save money and reduce air _____.

Solids are good **conductors** of thermal energy. When a solid is heated, the particles gain energy and vibrate more. Energy is **transferred** (passed) from one particle to the next because they are packed close together. Liquids and gases are not good conductors because their particles are quite far apart. Liquids and gases mostly transfer thermal energy by a process called **convection**.

Solids, liquids and gases **expand** when they are heated. This is because their particles begin to move faster and move further apart. They **contract** again as they get cooler.

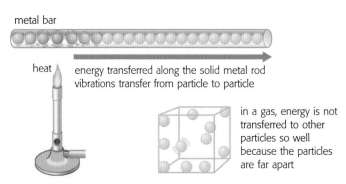

metal bar

heat

energy transferred along the solid metal rod vibrations transfer from particle to particle

in a gas, energy is not transferred to other particles so well because the particles are far apart

Solids conduct heat well. As they are heated, vibrations are passed from one particle to the next.

solids

liquids

gases

This model shows why liquids and gases are poor conductors. In solids, vibrations are passed easily from one particle to the next because they are close together. In liquids and gases, the particles are further apart and vibrations are not passed on as easily.

1 What happens to solids, liquids and gases when they are heated? What happens when they are cooled?

2 These words have had their vowels removed. What should they say?

cndctr   **cntrct**   **cnvctn**

3 Explain why solids are good conductors, but liquids and gases are not.

Copy and complete using these words:

liquids   transferred   solids
expand   gases

_____ are good conductors. Energy is _____ from one particle to the next because they are packed close together. _____ and _____ are not good conductors. Solids, liquids and gases _____ when they are heated.

When we heat a solid, the particles start to vibrate more and they move further apart. The solid expands as it gets hotter. If we keep heating it, the forces that hold the particles together get weaker. Eventually, the solid melts and becomes a liquid. The temperature at which this happens is called the **melting point**.

If we keep heating the liquid, the particles begin to move around even more quickly. Eventually, the forces that hold them together break apart and the liquid becomes a gas. The temperature at which this happens is called the **boiling point**.

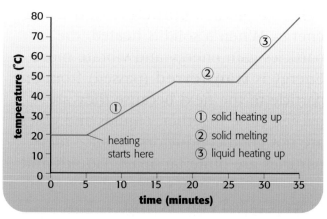

① solid heating up
② solid melting
③ liquid heating up

As a solid melts its temperature does not change. The thermal energy that is taken in is used to weaken the forces between the particles. The melting point of this solid is 47 °C.

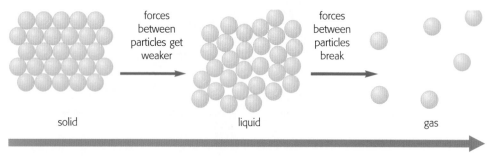

As a solid melts the forces between the particles get weaker and it becomes a liquid. If we keep heating the liquid the forces between the particles will break and it will change into a gas.

1 What do we call the temperature at which a solid changes into a liquid?

2 Unscramble these words:

    gilmnet   oigblin   ritevab

3 The boiling point of pure water is 100 °C. Sketch a graph like the one above to show how the temperature of pure water changes as it is heated from 50 °C to 120 °C.

Copy and complete using these words:

break   boiling point   weaker melting point

As we heat a solid, the forces between the particles get _____. The solid melts and becomes a liquid at its _____ _____. If we keep heating the liquid, the forces between the particles _____ apart. The liquid becomes a gas at its _____ _____.

What have I learnt?

1 Draw a temperature scale like the one on page 64. Write each of these temperatures in the correct place:

Cup of coffee (75 °C)

Freezing point of water (0 °C)

Boiling point of water (100 °C)

Human body temperature (37 °C)

2 Copy and complete this sentence:

If two things are different temperatures, thermal energy will flow from the _____ one to the _____ one.

3 Write down three reasons why we should try to save energy by insulating our homes.

4 Match up the beginnings and endings below to make complete sentences.

Beginnings

Solids are

Gases and liquids are

When solids, liquids and gases are heated

When solids, liquids and gases are cooled

Endings

they contract.

poor conductors of heat.

good conductors of heat.

they expand.

5 The graph below shows how the temperature of a substance changes as it is heated. What is the melting point of the substance, and what is its boiling point? How can you tell?

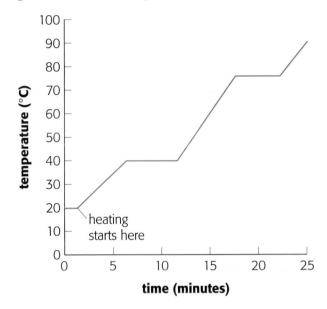

6 Imagine that you work on a TV quiz programme. Write ten questions for the programme about the things that you have met in this unit. Write them in the same style as the example below and remember to include the answers!

Q: What E describes what happens when solids, liquids and gases are heated?

A: Expand.

Magnets and electromagnets

What I should already know

- Magnets can be useful because they attract and repel things.
- Magnets attract magnetic materials.
- How to test the strength of a magnet.
- Current will only flow around an electrical circuit if the circuit is complete.

What I am going to meet in this unit

- A magnet has two ends called poles.
- Some materials are magnetic, other materials are non-magnetic.
- How compasses work.
- Magentism can be blocked by a magnetic material.
- All magnets have a magnetic field around them.
- Electromagnets and their uses.

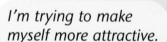

Why is your jacket covered with magnets?

I'm trying to make myself more attractive.

Magnets exert a **magnetic force** on other objects. **Magnetism** (magnetic force) is a non-contact force that can either be a push or a pull. Magnets attract **magnetic** materials like iron, steel, nickel, cobalt and iron oxide, but not all metals are magnetic materials. Magnets have no effect on **non-magnetic** materials like wood, plastic and copper.

Magnets have two ends called **poles**. If they can move, one end always points north. This is called the **north-seeking** pole. The other end of the magnet is called the **south-seeking** pole. As well as attracting magnetic materials, the pole of a magnet will:

o **attract** (pull) the opposite pole of another magnet

o **repel** (push) the like pole of another magnet.

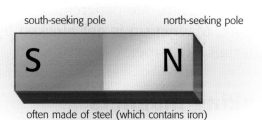

south-seeking pole   north-seeking pole

often made of steel (which contains iron)

1 What do we call the two ends of a magnet?

2 Unscramble these words:

   rpeel   geimtanc   slope

3 What would happen if you tried to put the north-seeking poles of two magnets together? Would the same thing happen if you put the opposite poles of two magnets together?

Copy and complete using these words:

non-magnetic   attract   magnetic repel   pole

Magnets attract _____ materials like iron but do nothing to _____ materials like plastic. They have a north-seeking _____ and a south-seeking pole. The pole of a magnet will _____ the opposite pole, and _____ the like pole, of another magnet.

Magnetism (magnetic force) is a non-contact force. Magnets attract **magnetic** materials without touching them.

Magnetism can be blocked by magnetic materials like steel. If we put a sheet of steel between a magnet and a paperclip, the magnet will not **attract** the paperclip. However, if we put a sheet of paper between a magnet and a paperclip, the paperclip will be attracted to the magnet. Magnetism is not blocked by **non-magnetic** materials like paper.

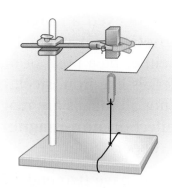

Non-magnetic materials like paper do not block magnetism.

Making magnets

A magnetic material can be **magnetised** (made into a magnet) by stroking it in a loop with the end of another magnet. It usually takes about 15 to 20 strokes to make a magnet.

Magnetic materials like steel block magnetism.

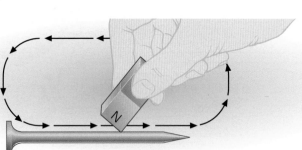

The magnetic material must be stroked in only one direction. At the end of each stroke, the magnet must be lifted away from the magnetic material.

1 What is magnetism?

2 How could you magnetise an iron nail?

3 Draw a diagram like the ones above to show what would happen if a thin piece of plastic was placed between a magnet and a paper clip. Explain what would happen.

Copy and complete using these words:

magnetic   magnetism   magnet magnetised   non-magnetic

_____ is a non-contact force. It can be blocked by _____ materials, but not by _____ materials. A magnetic material can be _____ by stroking it with the end of another _____.

All magnets have a region around them where a magnetic force can be felt. This is called a **magnetic field**. The Earth has a magnetic field because the centre of the Earth is made of molten (liquid) iron.

We can use iron filings to show us the magnetic field around a bar magnet. Iron filings are magnetic. When they are in the magnetic field of a bar magnet, they line up along the lines of force to show the **magnetic field lines**. The magnetic field lines are close together at the poles. This is where the magnetic field is strongest. As the magnetic field gets weaker, the field lines get further apart.

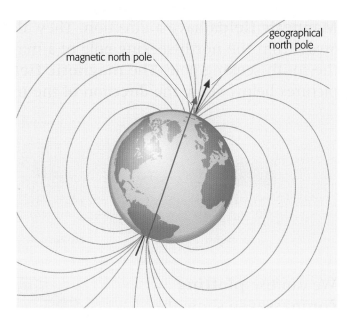

The Earth has a magnetic field.

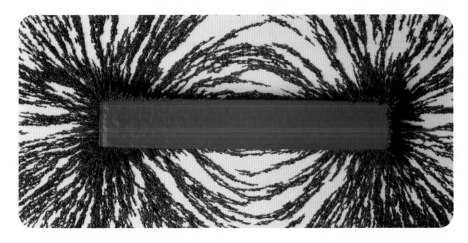

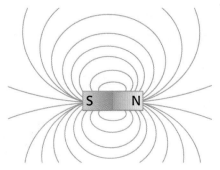

Iron filings show us the magnetic field lines around a bar magnet.

1 What is a magnetic field?

2 These words have had their vowels removed. What should they say?

   mgntc   fld lns

3 How can iron filings be used to show the magnetic field around a bar magnet?

Copy and complete using these words:

lines   field   poles   iron filings

All magnets have a magnetic _____ around them. We can use _____ _____ to show the magnetic field _____ around a bar magnet. The magnetic field is strongest at the _____.

73

More about magnetic fields

Magnetic fields have a direction. They always flow away from the north-seeking pole of a magnet, towards the south-seeking pole. The **magnetic field lines** in the pictures below show the direction of the magnetic fields:

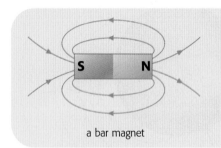

a bar magnet

two like poles repelling each other

two opposite poles attracting each other

We can use **plotting compasses** to show the direction of a magnetic field. We can also use them for **navigation** (finding which way to go), because they point towards the magnetic north pole of the Earth. If we know which way north is, we can work out which way we need to go.

A plotting compass shows the direction of a magnetic field.

1 Magnetic fields have a direction. Which pole of a magnet does the magnetic field flow towards?

2 Unscramble these words:

   macsops   **gavinitoan**

3 Explain how plotting compasses can be used for navigation.

Copy and complete using these words:

direction   south-seeking
navigation   north-seeking

Magnetic fields always point away from the _____ pole of a magnet, towards the _____ pole. Plotting compasses show the _____ of a magnetic field. We can use them for _____.

When electricity is passed through a coil of wire it has a magnetic field around it. We call the coil of wire a **solenoid**. The solenoid acts like a magnet. Because we have made a magnet using electricity, we say that we have made an **electromagnet**.

An electromagnet can be made stronger if we put a magnetic material in the **core** (centre) of the solenoid. We can also increase the strength of an electromagnet by:

o increasing the number of coils in the solenoid

o increasing the current.

Unlike normal magnets, electromagnets can be switched on or off. They are used in devices like electric bells, electric showers and cranes in scrap yards.

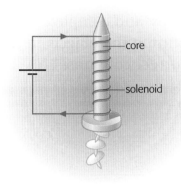

The iron nail in the core of the solenoid makes the magnetic field stronger.

The electromagnet in this crane has been switched on to pick up the car, and will be switched off to put it down somewhere else.

1 When electricity is passed through a coil of wire it acts like a magnet. What do we call the coil of wire?

2 These words have had their vowels removed. What should they say?

slnd   lctrmgnt

3 How are electromagnets different to normal magnets? Describe how this is useful in a device like a crane in a scrapyard.

Copy and complete using these words:

**current   coils   electromagnet
solenoid   magnetic**

When we pass electricity through a _____ we make an _____. We can make an electromagnet stronger by putting a _____ material in the solenoid's core, increasing the number of _____ or increasing the _____.

What have I learnt?

1 Copy and complete the table below by putting the objects in the list into the correct columns:

Magnetic materials	Non-magnetic materials

  wooden spoon

  iron nail

  piece of nickel

  cardboard box

  stainless steel cutlery

  plastic ball

2 Describe how you could magnetise an iron nail using a bar magnet.

3 Draw and label a diagram to show the magnetic field lines around a bar magnet.

4 Decide whether each statement below is true or false. Write them in your book, correcting the ones that are false.

  a Plotting compasses show the direction of a magnetic field.

  b A magnetic field always points towards the north-seeking pole of a magnet.

  c Plotting compasses point towards the magnetic south pole of the Earth.

5 List three ways that the strength of an electromagnet can be increased.

6 Imagine that you are an inventor. Design a device that uses a magnet or an electromagnet. Draw a picture of your device and explain how it works. How could your invention be used?

Light

What I should already know

- Light travels in straight lines.
- Some materials let light through. Other materials block the path of light.
- We see a shadow when an object blocks the path of light.
- Mirrors and other shiny surfaces reflect light.

What I am going to meet in this unit

- How light travels from a light source.
- How we see luminous and non-luminous objects.
- Transparent, translucent and opaque materials.
- The law of reflection.
- What happens when light is refracted or dispersed.
- How we see colours, and can change the colour of an object by using a filter.

I don't know why they bother. Light always travels faster than sound.

How does light travel?

Things that give out light energy are called **light sources**. We say that they are **luminous**. Light travels out from a light source in all directions, in straight lines called **rays**. It does not need to travel through a material. Light travels at 300 000 000 m/s. This is much faster than sound, which travels at 330 m/s.

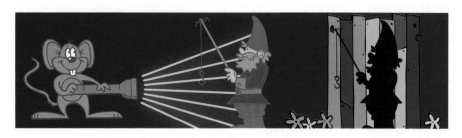

The rays of light are blocked by the gnome and a shadow forms. This shows that light travels in straight lines.

We see luminous objects when the rays of light that they give out enter our eyes. **Non-luminous** objects do not give out light. We see non-luminous objects because they **reflect** light rays that have been given out by light sources. The light rays bounce off non-luminous objects and into our eyes.

Sunita can see the lamp because the light that it gives out goes into her eyes. She can see the chocolate because it reflects the light from the lamp.

1 How does light travel out from a light source?

2 Unscramble these words:

noliusmu   asry   lefcret

3 In a thunderstorm, we always see lightning before we hear thunder. Explain why we see the lightning first. Include the speeds of sound and light in your answer.

Copy and complete using these words:

**sound   non-luminous   rays
reflect   material**

Light travels out from a light source in straight lines called _____. It does not need to travel through a _____ and travels much faster than _____. We see _____ objects because they _____ rays of light into our eyes.

We can sort materials into groups depending on what happens to light when it hits them:

Transparent materials

When light is shone at a **transparent** (see-through) material almost all of the light passes through it. Glass, Perspex and pure water are transparent materials.

Translucent materials

When light is shone at a **translucent** material only some of the light can pass through it. The rest is **absorbed** or **reflected**. Frosted glass is a translucent material.

Opaque materials

When light is shone at an **opaque** material most of the light is reflected from its surface. No light passes through the material, but some may be absorbed. Mirrors, books and people are opaque.

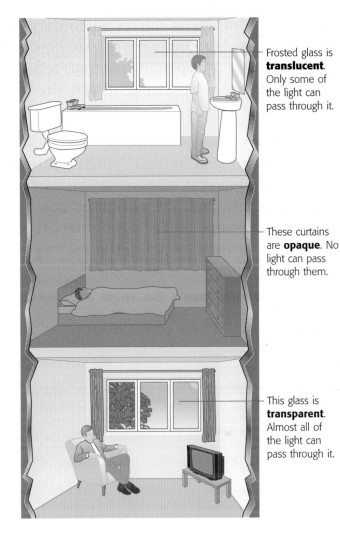

Frosted glass is **translucent**. Only some of the light can pass through it.

These curtains are **opaque**. No light can pass through them.

This glass is **transparent**. Almost all of the light can pass through it.

1 Give an example of a transparent material.

2 These words have had their vowels removed. What should they say?

   trnsprnt   trnslcnt   pq

3 Make three lists of things that you can see in your classroom: one of transparent materials, one of translucent materials and one of opaque materials.

Copy and complete using these words:

translucent   all   reflected
transparent   opaque   some

When light is shone at a _____ material almost _____ of the light can pass through it. Only _____ of the light can pass through a _____ material. No light passes through an _____ material. Most of it is _____.

We see non-luminous objects when they **reflect** light into our eyes. Opaque materials are best at reflecting light, but even transparent materials reflect some light. The smoother and shinier a surface, the more light it will reflect.

We can investigate reflection by shining a ray of light at a plane mirror (flat mirror). When the **incident ray** (the ray of light that is shone at the mirror) hits the mirror it is reflected. The **reflected ray** bounces off the mirror at the same angle to the **normal** (an imaginary line drawn at right angles to the mirror) as the incident ray. We say that:

the angle of incidence = the angle of reflection

This is called the **law of reflection**.

The surface of this lake is very smooth so it reflects light well.

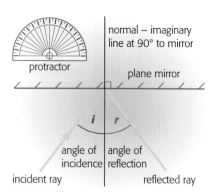

The angle of reflection is the same as the angle of incidence.

---

1 What do we call the imaginary line that is drawn at right angles to a plane mirror?

2 Unscramble these words:

   cenidniec   teilerconf

3 Draw a diagram like the one above, where the angle of incidence is 45°. What is the angle of reflection?

Copy and complete using these words:

incidence   reflected   incident
reflection   normal

When a ray of light is shone at a plane mirror, the _____ ray bounces off the mirror at the same angle to the _____ as the _____ ray. We say that the angle of _____ equals the angle of _____.

It's all about image!

When you look into a mirror you see an **image** of yourself because the mirror reflects light. The image looks as if it is behind the mirror and as far away from the mirror as you are, but it is the wrong way round. The mirror image has your left on your right and your right on your left.

The image in the mirror shows Andrew's left on the right and his right on the left.

Refraction

Light can be bent when it passes from one material into another. This is called **refraction**. When an incident ray is refracted it bends towards the **normal**. The angle of refraction is always smaller than the angle of incidence.

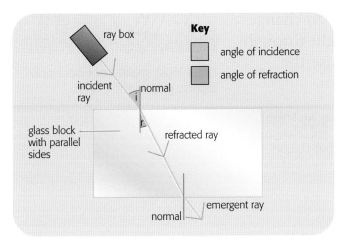

It is harder for light to pass through glass than through air. When the incident ray goes into the glass block, it slows down and bends towards the normal. When it leaves the glass block, it speeds up and bends away from the normal again.

1 When you look into a mirror, does your image show your right-hand side on the right or the left?

2 These words have had their vowels removed. What should they say?

   mg   **rfrctn**   **nrml**

3 What happens when a ray of light passes through a glass block? Why does this happen?

Copy and complete using these words:

material   **refraction**   **image**
normal   **reflected**

When light is _____ by a mirror we see an _____. It looks the same as the object but is the wrong way round. Light can be bent when it passes from one _____ into another. This is called _____. The incident ray bends towards the _____.

When a ray of white light is shone through a **prism** (triangular block of glass) we see a **spectrum** (the colours of the rainbow). The white light is **dispersed** (split up) into seven different colours. Each colour is refracted (bent) by a different amount.

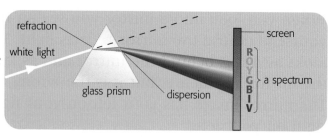

When white light is shone through a prism it is dispersed.

Objects look coloured because they **reflect** certain colours of light. Grass looks green because it only reflects green light. It **absorbs** all of the other colours in the spectrum. Objects that look white reflect all of the colours in the spectrum. Objects that look black absorb all of the colours in the spectrum.

We can use **filters** (pieces of coloured plastic) to change the colour of things. When we shine white light through a red filter we only see red light. This is because the filter absorbs the other colours in the spectrum.

Grass looks green because it only reflects green light.

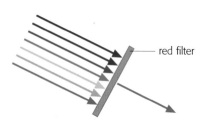

We see red light when we shine white light through a red filter because all of the other colours are absorbed.

1 What happens when you shine white light through a prism?

2 Why do black objects look black? Why do green objects look green?

3 What colour light would you see if you shone white light through a green filter? Explain your answer using the words below:

    absorbs   **spectrum**
    green light   **white light**

Copy and complete using these words:

reflects   **dispersed**   **filter**
prism   **refracted**

When a ray of white light is shone through a _____ it is _____. Each colour is _____ by a different amount. A green object looks green because it only _____ green light. A red _____ absorbs all of the colours of light except red.

What have I learnt?

1 a Is the Moon luminous or non-luminous? How do we see the Moon?

b Is the Sun luminous or non-luminous? How do we see the Sun?

2 Copy and complete the table below by deciding whether each item is transparent, translucent or opaque.

Transparent	Translucent	Opaque

muddy water
chocolate
pure water
frosted glass
perspex
a cat

3 Copy the diagram below and add labels to explain what the letters A to E show.

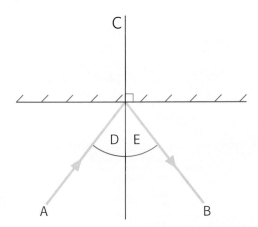

4 Draw a diagram to show what happens when a ray of light is refracted as it passes through a glass block.

5 Explain why a pair of blue jeans looks blue in white light. Which colours of light are absorbed by the jeans? Which colours are reflected?

6 One way to remember to order of the colours of light in the spectrum is to use this mnemonic:

Richard	**R**ed
Of	**O**range
York	**Y**ellow
Gave	**G**reen
Battle	**B**lue
In	**I**ndigo
Vain	**V**iolet

Write your own mnemonic to help you remember the order of the colours in

Sound and hearing

What I should already know

- Sound travels by vibrations through solids, liquids and gases.
- How to make the sound from a musical instrument louder or quieter.
- How to make the sound from a musical instrument higher or lower.
- We hear sounds when vibrations reach our ears.

What I am going to meet in this unit

- How sound travels.
- The difference between the pitch and the intensity of a sound.
- An oscilloscope shows wave patterns with different shapes for different sounds.
- Sound can't travel through a vacuum. It needs to travel through a material or a medium.
- How the human ear works.
- Sounds that are too loud can damage our ears.

No one can hear you scream in space!

How are sounds made?

Sound is a type of energy that travels as waves. A sound is made when something **vibrates** (shakes) and sends out waves of **sound energy**. We hear the sound when the waves reach our ears.

Sounds are described in two ways: pitch and intensity. The **pitch** of a sound tells you how high or low it is. When you play a guitar you can make the pitch of a note higher by making the string shorter, tightening it or using a thinner one. The **intensity** or loudness of a sound tells you how loud or quiet it is. The harder you hit a drum, the louder the sound.

When you **hit a drum the skin vibrates and makes a sound.**

Woodwind instruments like the flute have columns of air inside them. When you play them, the column of air vibrates and sounds are made.

1 **What is sound?**
2 **These words have had their vowels removed. What should they say?**

   chitp   stininyet   retvaibs

3 **When you hit a drum you hear a sound. How is the sound made? How does the sound travel to your ears? How could you make the sound louder?**

Copy and complete using these words:

**vibrates   intensity   energy
pitch   waves**

Sound is a type of _____ that travels as _____. It is made when something _____. We can describe sounds in two ways. The _____ of a sound tells us how high or low it is. The _____ of a sound tells us how loud or quiet it is.

An **oscilloscope** is a device that lets us 'see' what a sound looks like. It shows sounds as **wave patterns**. Different sounds produce waves with different shapes. The shapes of the waves tell us about the pitch and intensity of the sounds:

o The **amplitude** (height) of a wave tells us about the **intensity** of a sound. The bigger the sound wave, the louder the sound.

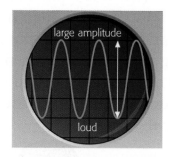 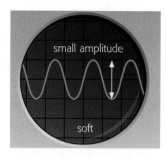

The sound making the wave pattern on the left is louder than the one on the right.

o The **frequency** of the waves (the number of waves on the screen) tells us about the **pitch** of a sound. The higher the frequency, the higher the sound.

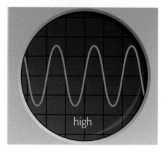 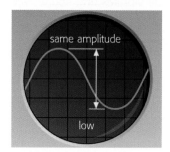

The sound making the wave pattern on the left has a higher pitch than the one on the right.

1 What is an oscilloscope?

2 These words have had their vowels removed. What should they say?

frqncy   mpltd   wv pttrn

3 Draw a picture of a wave pattern that is made by a loud sound with a low pitch. Do the same for a quiet sound with a high pitch.

Copy and complete using these words:

**wave   frequency   amplitude
oscilloscopes   shapes**

_____ show us sounds as _____ patterns. Different sounds produce waves with different _____. The _____ of a wave tells us about the intensity of a sound. The _____ of a wave tells us about the pitch.

Unlike light, sound needs a material or **medium** to travel through. Sound is carried by **vibrations** so it needs to be carried by a solid, liquid or gas. The vibrations pass from one particle in the medium to the next until they reach our ears. Sound can't travel through a **vacuum** (empty space) because there are no particles to carry the vibrations.

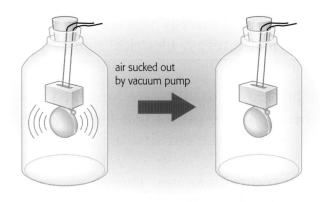

air sucked out by vacuum pump

When a bell rings in a jar of air we can hear the sound. If the air is sucked out of the jar we can no longer hear the bell because it is in a vacuum.

Sound travels at different speeds through different materials. The particles of a solid are packed close together so vibrations are passed on quickly. In a gas the particles are quite far apart. Sound travels through a solid much faster than through a gas.

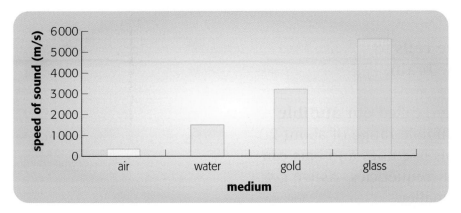

This bar chart shows how quickly sound travels through different materials.

1 Why does sound need a medium to travel through?

2 Unscramble these words:

    ucvuam   **imudem**   **tabivoirn**

3 Why can't sound travel through space? Include these words in your answer:

    medium   **vacuum**
    vibrations   **particles**

Copy and complete using these words:

vibrations   **gas**   **particle**
medium   **solid**   **vacuum**

Sound needs a _____ to travel through. It can't travel through a _____. When a sound travels through a solid, liquid or gas, _____ are passed on from one _____ to the next. Sound travels through a _____ faster than through a _____.

When **sound energy** reaches our ears it is changed into **electrical energy**. Electrical signals are then sent to the brain and we 'hear' the sound:

Vibrating air particles are funnelled into the ear by the **pinna** (ear flap) towards the **ear drum**.

⬇

The ear drum vibrates. The vibrations are passed on to three tiny bones in the middle ear that **magnify** (increase) the vibration.

⬇

The **cochlea** contains fluid and tiny hairs. When the fluid vibrates, these hairs move.

⬇

This movement causes **nerve cells** to send electrical signals to the **brain**.

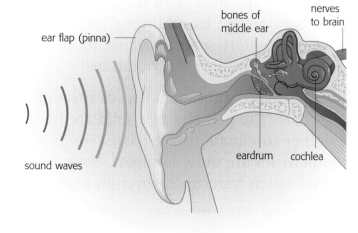

The sounds that we can hear are called our **audible range**. Most people have an audible range of about 20 to 20 000 Hz, but some animals like dogs and bats can hear sounds with much higher frequencies. As we get older, our audible range gets smaller.

1 What is sound energy changed into in our ears?

2 These words have had their vowels removed. What should they say?

pnn   r drm   cchl   nrv clls

3 Draw a flow diagram like the one above to explain how we hear sounds. Make sure that you describe what each part of the ear does.

Copy and complete using these words:

**bones   electrical   vibrations
cochlea   ear drum**

When sound energy enters our ears, the _____ are passed on to the cochlea by the _____ _____ and three _____ in the middle ear. The movement of tiny hairs in the _____ then causes nerve cells to send _____ signals to the brain.

8L.5 Too loud!

Our ears are very sensitive. If we are exposed to loud **noises** (nasty or loud sounds) for a long time our hearing can be damaged. We can use sound meters to measure how loud sounds are in units called **decibels** (**dB**). Our hearing can be damaged if we are exposed to sounds above 90 dB.

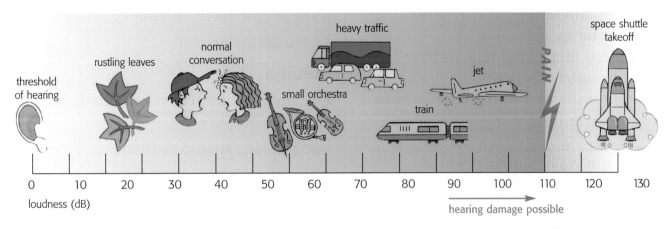

There are different ways that you can protect your hearing. Some of them are listed below:

o Fit your home with double glazing

o Use thick, soft materials for curtains and carpets

o Don't have your personal stereo on too loud

o Wear ear defenders if you have a noisy job.

This sign warns us to wear ear defenders to protect our ears.

---

1 What can happen if you are exposed to loud noises for a long time?

2 Unscramble these words:

becdeils   iesnos

3 Double glazed windows have an air gap between two panes of glass. Why are they better at protecting us from too much noise than normal windows?

Copy and complete using these words:

decibels   protect   noises
measure   hearing

Our _____ can be damaged if we are exposed to loud _____ for a long time. Sound meters _____ how loud sounds are in units called _____ (dB). We can _____ our hearing by fitting double glazing or wearing ear defenders.

1 Decide whether each statement is true or false. Write them in your book, correcting the ones that are false.

   a Sound is a type of force that travels as waves.
   b A sound is made when something vibrates and sends out waves of sound energy.
   c The pitch of a sound tells us how loud or quiet it is.
   d The intensity of a sound tells us how low or high it is.

2 Look at the wave patterns below. Which of the wave patterns is made by a sound that is:

   a Loud and high pitched.
   b Quiet and low pitched.
   c Loud and low pitched.

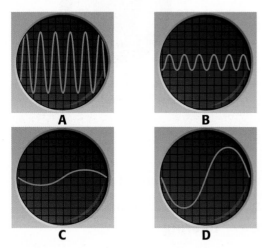

3 Explain why sound travels faster through a solid than through a gas.

4 Match up the beginnings and endings below to make complete sentences.

   Beginnings

   Vibrations in the air enter the ear

   When sound energy enters our ears

   Most people have an audible range

   As we get older

   Endings

   it is changed into electrical signals that go to the brain.

   our audible range gets smaller.

   and make the ear drum vibrate.

   of about 20 Hz to 20 000 Hz.

5 What do decibels measure?

6 Write a safety leaflet about sound for next year's Year 8 students. Try to answer these questions in your leaflet:

   o What happens if we are exposed to loud sounds for a long time?
   o How can we measure the loudness of sounds?
   o How can we protect our hearing in the home?
   o How can we protect our hearing at work?

Glossary

Words in italic have their own glossary entry.

A

absorbed Taken in by the blood to be used by the body.

aerobic respiration *Respiration* using oxygen.

alveoli Air sacs in the lungs where *gas exchange* takes place.

amplitude The height of a wave.

antibiotics Drugs that kill *micro-organisms* in your body.

antibodies Chemicals made by *white blood cells* to help fight *pathogens*.

artificial immunity When we are *immune* to an *infectious disease* because we have been given a *vaccine*.

atoms The building blocks of *elements*.

audible range The range of sound that a person can hear.

B

bacteria Type of *micro-organism* that is single-celled, and doesn't have a nucleus.

balanced diet Eating enough of each of the seven nutrients.

biological weathering *Weathering* of rocks by plants and animals.

boiling point The *temperature* at which a liquid changes state to a gas.

C

Celsius A scale used to measure *temperature* in degrees Celsius (°C).

chemical reaction A change in which new substances are made, that can't be turned back easily.

chemical weathering *Weathering* of rocks by *chemical reactions*.

circulatory system Organ system that transports things around our bodies in the blood.

community The plants and animals that share a *habitat*.

compound Substances made from *atoms* of more than one *element*, chemically joined.

conduction When *thermal energy* is passed from one particle to the next.

consumer A living organism that eats other plants and animals.

D

decibel (dB) Unit of loudness.

deposition When *sediment* is laid down after *transportation*.

digestion Process by which our bodies break down food so that we can use the nutrients in it.

digestive system Organ system where *digestion* takes place.

disinfectant Chemicals that kill *micro-organisms*, that are used outside the body.

dispersion When white light is split into a *spectrum* of seven different colours.

E

electromagnet A *magnet* that is made using a *solenoid*.

element Substance that is made from only one type of *atom*.

erosion *Weathering* of rocks and *transportation* of *sediment*.

exhale Remove air from the lungs.

extrusive igneous rock *Igneous* rock formed on the Earth's surface.

F

filter (light) A *translucent* material that is a certain colour, and absorbs certain colours of light.

food chain Diagram that shows us who eats who.

food web Diagram that shows how all the *food chains* in a *community* join together.

formula A combination of *symbols* for different *elements* or *molecules*. Tells us which *elements* a *compound* is made from, and in what ratio.

fossils The remains of dead plants or animals that have been trapped in *sedimentary rocks*.

freeze-thaw weathering *Weathering* of rocks caused by water freezing and thawing many times.

frequency The number of waves.

fungi Type of *micro-organism* that feeds off other living organisms. Most are bigger than *bacteria*.

G

gas exchange Exchange of oxygen and carbon dioxide in the *alveoli* of the lungs.

glucose A store of chemical energy that is a *reactant* in *respiration*.

H

habitat Place where an organism lives.

heating Transfer of *thermal energy*.

hertz (Hz) Unit of *frequency*.

I

igneous rock Type of rock that forms when *magma* cools and solidifies.

immune Your *white blood cells* 'remember' how to make *antibodies* against a certain *pathogen*.

incident ray Ray of light that moves towards something.

infectious disease A disease that can be passed from one organism to another, caused by *micro-organisms*.

inhale Take air into the lungs.

intensity The loudness of a sound.

intrusive igneous rock *Igneous rock* formed under the Earth's surface.

J

joule (J) The unit for measuring energy (1 kJ = 1000 J).

L

lava *Magma* that has reached the Earth's surface.

law of reflection The angle of incidence = the angle of reflection.

M

magma Hot molten rock under the Earth's surface.

magnet Something that exerts a *magnetic force* on other objects.

magnetic field The region around a *magnet* where a *magnetic force* can be felt.

magnetic force A non-contact force that can either be a push or a pull. Also called magnetism.

magnetic material A material that experiences a force in a *magnetic field*.

melting point The *temperature* at which a solid changes state to a liquid.

metals *Elements* that are grouped on the left-hand side of the *periodic table*. They are usually solids at room *temperature*.

metamorphic rock Type of rock that forms when rocks are changed by heat and pressure.

micro-organisms Living organisms that are too small to be seen unless you use a microscope. Also called microbes.

mixture Contains two or more substances that are not chemically joined.

molecule Group of *atoms* that are chemically joined.

N

natural barriers The first line of defence that our bodies have against *pathogens*. They include skin and tears.

natural immunity When we are *immune* to an *infectious disease*, without having been given a *vaccine*.

non-metals *Elements* that are grouped on the right-hand side of the *periodic table*. Many of them are gases at room *temperature*.

normal An imaginary line at 90° to a mirror or lens.

north-seeking poles The pole of a *magnet* that is attracted to the Earth's north pole.

O

onion skin weathering *Weathering* of rocks caused by them expanding during the day when they are heated by the Sun, and contracting at night when it is cooler.

opaque A material that light can't pass through.

oscilloscope A device that lets us 'see' what a sound looks like.

P

pasteurisation Killing *micro-organisms* in milk by *sterilisation*.

pathogens *Micro-organisms* that cause *infectious diseases*.

periodic table A table of all the different *elements*, grouped together by their properties.

physical weathering *Weathering* of rocks by changes in the *temperature* of the environment.

pitch How high or low a sound is.

population The number of organisms of a certain species living in a *habitat*.

porous Has little spaces in its structure that water can get into.

prism A glass block that is usually triangular. Splits white light into a *spectrum*.

producer A green plant that makes its own food.

products Substances that are made in a *chemical reaction*.

pyramid of numbers A diagram that shows the number of organisms in each *population* in a *food chain*.

Q

quadrat A 1 m square frame that is used to sample the number of plants in a *habitat*.

R

reactants Substances that react in a *chemical reaction*, to make the *products*.

reflected ray A light ray that has been reflected.

reflects Light bounces off it.

refraction Bending of light as it passes into a different material.

respiration The *chemical reaction* that releases energy from food such as *glucose*.

respiratory system Organ system that brings oxygen into our bodies, and removes carbon dioxide.

rock cycle The process by which old rocks are recycled into new rocks.

S

sediment Rock fragments.

sedimentary rock Type of rock that forms when layers of *sediment* are cemented together.

Glossary

solenoid A coil of wire with electricity passing through it, that acts like a *magnet*.

spectrum The colours of the rainbow that combine to make white light.

sterilisation Killing *micro-organisms* by heating things to high *temperatures*.

symbol One or two letters used to represent an *element*.

T

temperature How hot or cold something is.

thermal conductor Material that conducts heat well.

thermal energy Heat energy.

thermal insulator Material that does not conduct heat well.

thermometer Used to measure temperature.

translucent A material that only lets some light through.

transparent A material that lets almost all light through.

transportation When *sediment* is carried away by water, or by the wind.

V

vaccine An injection of weak or dead *micro-organisms*, that makes your body produce *antibodies* against a *pathogen*. Makes you *immune* to an *infectious disease*.

vacuum An empty space that doesn't contain any particles.

virus Type of *micro-organism* that is not a cell, and is smaller than *bacteria* and *fungi*.

W

weathering When rocks are broken into smaller pieces.

white blood cells Cells in the blood that help fight *infectious diseases*.

word equation An equation that uses words to explain what happens in a *chemical reaction*.

Index